Books of Merit

The Perfect Order of Things

ALSO BY DAVID GILMOUR

Back on Tuesday
How Boys See Girls
An Affair with the Moon
Lost Between Houses
Sparrow Nights
A Perfect Night to Go to China
The Film Club

DAVID GILMOUR

The Perfect

Order

of Things

A Novel

THOMAS ALLEN PUBLISHERS
TORONTO

Certain portions of this book have appeared in a different form
in other publications.

Library and Archives Canada Cataloguing in Publication

Gilmour, David, 1949–
        The perfect order of things / David Gilmour.

ISBN 978-0-88762-807-8

I. Title.

PS8563.I56P48 2011   c813'.54   C2011-903231-7

Editor: Patrick Crean
Jacket design and front jacket photo: Michel Vrána
Back jacket photo: pixhook / istockphoto.com

Published by Thomas Allen Publishers,
a division of Thomas Allen & Son Limited,
390 Steelcase Road East,
Markham, Ontario L3R 1G2 Canada

www.thomasallen.ca

ONTARIO ARTS COUNCIL
CONSEIL DES ARTS DE L'ONTARIO

Canada Council
for the Arts

The publisher gratefully acknowledges the support of
The Ontario Arts Council for its publishing program.

We acknowledge the support of the Canada Council for the Arts, which
last year invested $20.1 million in writing and publishing throughout Canada.

We acknowledge the Government of Ontario through the
Ontario Media Development Corporation's Ontario Book Initiative.

We acknowledge the financial support of the Government of Canada
through the Canada Book Fund for our publishing activities.

11 12 13 14 15   5 4 3 2 1

Text printed on a 100% PCW recycled stock
Printed and bound in Canada

For Sam Hiyate
Agent *par excellence*

Nowhere do so many flowers grow as in a cemetery.

— MARCEL PROUST

The Perfect Order of Things

1

What Else Did I Miss?

A few years ago I found myself in the south of France. It was early winter and I was writing a travel piece for one of those glossy magazines you read on airplanes when you're stuck on the tarmac or trying to terminate a conversation with a chatty neighbour. On the way back to Paris and the plane home, my train stopped in Toulouse. On the spur of the moment I yanked my bag off the rack and jumped down. Storing my things in a luggage locker, I started up the rue Bayard, past the American Express where, almost forty years earlier, I had gone daily hoping for a letter from Raissa Shestatsky. Sometimes yes, but mostly no.

I drifted through the narrow red-brick streets until I arrived at the Père Léon, the café where I went to read her letters or, when there weren't any, to think about her and to wonder if I'd ever make love to her again. I was about to go in—for some absurd reason I expected the same waiters to be there—but instead I kept walking. During those unhappy months so many years earlier, it had seemed as though I were fixed to a miniature railway track that ran from my apartment on rue Victor Dequé to a table in the window of the Café Père Léon. But I had never seen what was on the *other side* of the café. I had no curiosity; like a car locked in a single gear, I felt only the absence of Raissa and her slender limbs from my bed.

So this time I walked further on; and there, not fifty yards away, like the opening chords of a Beethoven symphony, a wide, beautiful river, a half mile across, opened up in front of me. I swear I'd never seen it before, never even suspected it was there. A cargo boat drifted dreamily downstream; on the far bank, a tiny red light flickered off and on.

How could I have missed it, this green jewel that seemed wider than the Mississippi? For six months I'd lived in Toulouse and I'd seen nothing except the furious wallpaper inside my head: its drastic scenarios, its pornographic reruns. What *else* had my misery blinded me to?

So over the next few months (it was quite gradual, I remember) I decided, almost in the spirit of settling a personal debt, a debt to one*self*, to go back to *other* places where I'd suffered, this time with my eyes open and, more important, pointed outwards. Go back and see what's what.

But where to start. Something old or something new? Which old mansion of horror should I visit first? A boarding school, a Ferris wheel spinning backwards into the night, a park in Los Angeles, a busy office at a film festival, a country house with a broken spine. . . ?

Happily, the decision was made for me. One day, leafing through the newspaper at my ex-wife's house—M. was making dinner for me and our daughter, who was home from university that weekend—I happened across the picture of a barracuda-faced woman emerging from a limousine. Below, a caption read, OPERA HOUSE FUNDRAISER CHARGED WITH MISAPPROPRIA-TION. There was something familiar about the face, the exaggerated cheekbones, the sleek, brushed-back hair, but I couldn't recall what it was. I moved on to the next item. But the face called me back. *"Misappropriation of funds."* I took another look: it was Clarissa Bentley. And apparently up to her old tricks again. Beneath those ample breasts beat the heart of a woman so unpleasant even the Borgias would have hesitated to have lunch with her.

A few days later, Clarissa on my mind, I wandered up to my old high school. I passed through a set of regal blue doors, the school crest embedded in the floor like a giant Roman coin, and stepped into the interior courtyard. Just across from me was a squat, three-storey brick building. I was an unhappy boarder there for a brief period in 1966, the year the Beatles came to Toronto. I say brief because I ran away that October after only a few weeks. I ran away, let me say it simply, because a young girl went up the

Ferris wheel with me as my girlfriend and when she came back down, she was someone else's. It was the first romantic betrayal of my life.

But I'm getting ahead of myself. Let me go back to that summer cottage in Grassmere when I was fifteen. Dew-damp mornings, pretty girls in canoes, dances in town. And those sounds! I have never forgotten those sounds. Stones crackling under the tires of the family car as we made our way down the driveway, tree branches brushing the sides. At night you could hear everything across the water: people talking on their docks, a screen door banging shut. A fish slapping the water. These nights remain haunting for me with their whispers of "You are missing something, you are missing something."

Nodding my head to the satisfying clank-clank of Ringo's cowbell in "I Call Your Name," I was lying on my mother's bed at the far end of the house when I heard her calling me from the kitchen. A phone call. Long-distance, hurry, hurry.

It was a girl I barely knew, Clarissa Bentley. Her father was a "big shot" in the movie business.

"I just broke up with my boyfriend," she said.

Even at that age I recognized the moment when a fresh moon might be rising in the sky. Looking out the picture window, at the yellow Van Gogh fields descending to the forest, I said, "That's too bad."

"No, it's not," she said, and inhaled sharply.

"Are you smoking?" I asked.

"Everybody smokes."

"Where are your parents?"

"My father lets me smoke in the house. He knows what'd happen if he didn't."

I pondered that for a moment. The lake glimmering like broken glass behind the trees.

"So are you coming down to the city or what?" she said.

My mother, her bright red shirt tied at the waist like a Caribbean chanteuse, was making a tomato sandwich in the kitchen.

"Who was that?" she said.

I liked my mother; I liked talking to her. "A girl I hardly know," I said. "She just broke up with her boyfriend."

"Ah," she replied, keeping her gaze deliberately on the chopping board.

My father was sick that summer and sometimes my mother would fold her long brown legs into our Chevrolet and drive for two hours south to the hospital in Toronto to see him. Which meant that my older brother, Dean, and I had the house to ourselves for the weekend. We played the stereo at full blast, drove old golf balls into the ravine, fired hunting rifles into the garbage dump, talked about girls, and once took a drive along a lonely country back road in my father's little blue Morris. That night, the night my mother left for Toronto, we went to the Saturday night dance at Hidden Valley in the boat.

"Remember," Dean said, "if I give you the signal, find another way to get home."

But the girl didn't show up or showed up with another boy and he didn't give me the signal that night. The two of us puttered home under the stars, the lake motionless and warm as soup. We tied up at the dock, cut through the spooky forest, broke out into a field beneath the moonlight, and climbed through the wet grass to our house, which gleamed like a jewel at the top of the hill.

I was only there a few minutes when the phone rang. I was downstairs, lying on the couch, staring at the knotholes in the ceiling. Dean was upstairs listening to an American baseball game on his bedside maroon radio. A lonely sound.

I picked up the phone expecting my mother, but when I heard the voice, again that feeling, the sensation of a bright moon rising in the sky, filled my head.

"What are you doing?" Clarissa Bentley asked. Her voice was as clear as if she were in the next room.

"I was at a dance."

"Did you meet anybody?"

"No, actually, I didn't." Then I thought, no, that was the wrong thing to say; that created entirely the wrong impression, and I flashed on those boys at the dance, a cluster of them by the railing, local kids, one of them finally tearing himself away, crossing the floor and asking a city girl to dance, only to make the same excruciating walk, droop-tailed, back across the floor to his friends. Refused.

"That's probably pretty unusual for you," Clarissa said. "You strike me as a real playboy."

The moon rose still higher.

She said, "I know a girl who knows you."

"Yeah?"

"She thinks you're going to be really good-looking when you grow up."

It was a curious compliment, like a razor blade tucked in a candy bar. First you felt good but then you wondered. Realizing it, or hearing what, in fact, she'd just said, Clarissa went on, "I like how you say *actually*. It's sort of English."

I could hear the baseball game upstairs. Someone had just hit the ball.

"Why don't you come down here?" Clarissa said. The air fizzed around the radio announcer's voice. The sound of life happening elsewhere.

"Down there?"

"Yes."

"When?"

"Tonight," she said matter-of-factly.

"Tonight?"

"You could hitchhike." She was smoking a cigarette. "We could sleep in my parents' bed."

A few minutes later, I went up the stairs and walked down the dark hall to Dean's room. I was older now, more mature than I had been only fifteen minutes before. He lay on his blue bed, his arm behind his head. In the announcer's American voice, in the ghostly sound of thousands of people behind it, you could see the brightly lit field, the players trotting in their white uniforms.

"Was that that chick?" Dean said. He turned his face toward me. He must have been eating chocolate again because his skin had broken out afresh.

I said, "I think I'm going to hitchhike to Toronto."

Then he said something cruel about my ears. I looked at him speechlessly.

"I'm going to get in shit for this," he said, as if we'd been talking about it for weeks. But that's not what he was angry about. It was inconceivable to me then that, being two years older, he *could* be unhappy. I started down the stairs. I could hear him get off the bed. I took the last few steps two at a time. I tore through the kitchen, through the living room and out the front door, the screen door banging behind me, and started up the driveway. I got to the first bend and glanced over my shoulder. Dean was standing in the doorway in his underwear, the living room lit up behind him. Then I plunged into the darkness, the trees overhead, the stones under my feet, until I reached the main road that led to town and beyond.

I arrived at Clarissa's address just as it was getting light. It was a big white apartment building on the edge of Forest Hill. A brightly lit lobby; black leather couches, abstract paintings. I pressed her number. A car drove by outside in the street. I pressed the number again. The lock on the door clicked once, then twice.

"Clarissa?" I said, bending over the speaker. No answer. I tried the door; it opened. And then I went inside.

She had done it before. You could tell. The way she took her clothes off and got into bed. But you could also tell that she was acting a bit. Then she talked about her boarding school in Switzerland, about having dinner once with Alfred Hitchcock; then she lit a cigarette and sat in a chair with no clothes on and told me a movie star had a crush on her, that he'd invited her to his cabin in New Mexico but her mother had found out and phoned the movie star and ruined everything. During these stories I had the feeling I was being lied to, that something *like* these stories had happened, only in a smaller, less spectacular way. But of course that's true for almost everything you think about other people's lives. Always smaller, always lonelier than you imagine.

I waited for her to bring up her ex-boyfriend, and I suspected that would be a lie too, whatever she told me. A particular lie with a particular slant. All her lies had the same slant, away from her, always toward someone else.

And I wished she would put some clothes on.

I knew her ex-boyfriend. Bill Cardelle was a party boy with a dash of red colouring in each cheek as if life or nature had given him an extra dose of vitality. He was a boy I'd never be like, a boy you saw in the halls at school and thought, "I'd be happy if I looked like that." But my hair was too curly for a proper Beatles haircut, my jackets always rose up at the back ("Don't slouch, dear!") and I couldn't dance like Bill Cardelle. At parties, even the boys watched him dance, not directly but with quick furtive glances between sips on a straw. In his white chinos and Oxford shirts and oxblood shoes, he had it all. Except for one thing: he wasn't very bright. I adored him because he was gorgeous; he admired me because I was smarter than he was; and for a time, while I tutored him in Latin, we were friends.

I telephoned Dean long-distance at Grassmere the next morning and I noticed in his voice a slightly different tone and it took me many months to understand what that tone was—an almost unwilling approbation that would be the beginning of a whole new kind of problem between us. He was eating an apple, sounding matter-of-fact, but what caught my ear, what mattered to me, was that I could hear him *trying* to sound matter-of-fact.

"So you guys stayed up really late?" which was his way of asking me if I'd fucked her. And when I said yes, pretty late, and felt a flush of pleasure (vanity), I could also tell that he had hoped that wasn't going to be the answer.

"So when are you coming home?" he asked. And in this too, things were different. Because normally he would have just ordered me around, told me to get back now.

I said that I'd get there for sure before Mother got home.

"Let's hope you don't run into her down there," and for the first time ever it was like we were talking shop as equals.

I said, "Yeah, that'd be something." We both had a good laugh over that one, longer than it deserved.

Then he said, "Don't fuck me on this, okay?" and I said, "You're a great guy, Kiv." That was his pet name; only my mother and I called him that, and only when he was being soft enough to let us.

And then I put the phone down and went back into the living room. Clarissa was standing by the window; below you could see the ravine and on the other side of the ravine, the Jewish quarter with their big houses and wonderful deep backyards. She said, "Let's go steal something."

It must have been a week or so later that I came down to the city with my brown suitcase to stay with my uncle,

Laddie. He was the family disgrace, plastered by noon every day. He had squandered his intelligence, his dark good looks, even a career as a hockey player. (I heard more than once, always in shaming tones, that he'd been invited to try out as a goalie for the Toronto Maple Leafs.) But his late wife, Ellen, was a kindly soul and had died before she could come to despise him, leaving behind a monthly, untouchable stipend, enough for Laddie to tipple himself to death more or less un-interfered with. And like many charming drunks, he'd quickly found a simple, decent woman to look after him, who saw, behind his puffy features and coarse humour, the classy educated gentleman he had once been and, in the grips of a ferocious hangover, could still be. A man who could quote Horace with his head in the toilet bowl.

My mother, who was Laddie's sister, knew I was going to Toronto to "see a girl" and that romantic streak in her, the streak that allowed her to stay with my father despite his infidelities (he fucked her best friend on the couch at Grassmere early one morning when he thought, incorrectly, she was asleep in the far wing of the house), let her drive me to the bus station in Huntsville. She was a woman who simply could never say no to love, even to her fifteen-year-old son.

I haven't described Clarissa. I'll leave that to you, except to say that with her black eye makeup, her short "French" haircut, she struck me, from the first time I saw her in the kitchen at a Christmas party, as a girl out of my league. And yet how odd it is that in only a matter of days she went from being a girl I could never "get" to a girl I assumed belonged with me.

Her good looks—and her "big shot" father—got her a job as a model at the Exhibition, a giant old-fashioned fair at the edge of Lake Ontario. On warm summer evenings, tingling with the excitement of the city, of being caught up in and fluent in its swirl, I rattled downtown in the streetcar to see her. Wandering under the huge gates of the Exhibition, through the crowds, the bangs and pops and shrieks and swoops of rides and games, I felt that I was being pulled toward the centre of life; and at that centre there was Clarissa Bentley, a human mannequin who stood motionless on a slowly revolving podium in the Automotive Building. Wearing a pink dress or a blue jumper or jeans with a candy-cane top, she was the object of scrutiny—would she blink, would she twitch, could you make her smile?—for the parade of humanity, men mostly, occasionally dragging their plump wives and bored children among the new-model Chevrolets and Buicks and Cadillacs. Having a beautiful girlfriend is a certain kind of delicious when you're young, and that moment when the podium ground gradually to a halt, when Clarissa's arms came to life, a smile crossed her heavily made-up features ("Johnnie, look at that!"), that moment when, carefully, she stepped down from the dais, one step, then another, then another, and came over to me, to *me*, that single moment quite lifted me from who I used to be and made me, I was sure, into someone new. The life I had always been owed.

The summer advanced. I have a photograph from that time, a coloured picture taken in a booth, me in a candy-coloured jacket and a straw boater, Clarissa in profile. I put it in a plastic gadget that lit up when you put it to your eye and pushed a button. I carried it around in my pocket like a passport.

And then one afternoon a boy from school, Justin Strawbridge, took me to the Place Pigalle, a gloomy downstairs tavern where, he said, we could get "served," the drinking age in those days being twenty-one. I hated the taste of draft beer, it made me shiver with disgust. But I loved getting "served" and I loved doing things with Justin Strawbridge and so I drank and drank and gradually it seemed to me I was a very interesting, daring fellow.

And after Justin left (he had an errand to do for his unpleasant mother), I wandered through the twilight bar, talking to people, even sitting down once at a crowded table until I found myself talking to the back of an engineering student. But I didn't take it personally. I let the sweep of things take me here and there.

It was such a gorgeous night when I emerged hours later, the sky a luminous, inexpressible blue, a sliver of moon hanging over the lake. So beautiful I couldn't stand to leave it, and I walked all the way down to the Exhibition. The moon rose in the sky, the stars came out, the city was wrapped in a bubble of density and meaning. Passing under the Exhibition gates (they loomed like a canyon overhead), I slalomed through the caramel-sweet air and children and exuberant young men. A double-decker Ferris wheel spun backwards into the night.

Clarissa waited for me outside the auto pavilion. She was chatting to another model, a girl in a red sweater with eyes too big for her bony skull; and it seemed to me that this girl spoke to me in a rather supercilious manner, as if she'd gone from not knowing me to not liking me in about forty-five seconds.

I wasn't as indulgent this time as I'd been with the engineering student, and I must have said something (I had quite the tongue back then), because she walked off without saying goodbye to either of us.

"Somebody's been drinking," Clarissa said. We started across the midway, the Saturday night crowd swollen and somehow more aggressive than other nights. Drifting in and out of the mob, fifty yards ahead of us, was Clarissa's old boyfriend, Bill Cardelle, coming this way.

I didn't know if they'd seen each other since he dumped her, but she wouldn't look at him, kept looking around the crowd as if she was expecting someone. But Bill, being Bill, eased his way through it, wasn't put off by her one-word answers, his hair falling just so over his forehead, his white chinos fashionably high up on the ankle and a pink shirt which, on anyone else, would have looked, well, you know. And after a while they fell into a conversation, friends in common, other couples, and the three of us, at my suggestion, made our way over to the Ferris wheel.

There was a messy lineup, couples changing their mind amidst a great deal of hilarity, teenagers butting in. I struck up a conversation with a grey-haired man and his wife. I did it, I think, to show Clarissa how easy, how confident I was with people, my gift of the gab. But it was my undoing, this gift of the gab, because while I was talking, Clarissa and Bill somehow got onto the Ferris wheel before me; down went the bar, *clank*, and the wheel moved up a notch. I got on. *Clank*. Then behind me the grey-haired man and his wife, who seemed not so interesting after all.

The ride started. Up, up, up we went; all the way to the top, where you could see the yellow clock tower of my school, like an owl's eye, staring at me. And then with a rush of screams and exploding lights, down we went, around and around and around. I could see in the chair just above me that their heads, Bill's and Clarissa's, were bent close together, as if to hear better; she was asking him questions; he'd answer and then pull his head back to see her reaction and then she'd look at him, not saying anything. I sensed that I was in terrible danger; panic whipped through my body like a pinball. Around and around and around we went. It went on forever, this infernal ride, and with every revolution I could feel her moving away from me.

They got off first, and when I joined them, staggering a little theatrically, I could see that they were waiting on something, she looking at him, Bill looking down at his loafers. And my mouth went completely dry.

Bill was dim but he wasn't vicious, and so he stood off at a decent distance while she told me. "I want to be with Bill now," she said, and there was, Clarissa being Clarissa, a hint of impatience, the same I'd heard in her voice when she asked me, Was I coming down to see her in the city, as if, in this case, she wanted to get this part of the evening over with (me) and "get on with things."

Bill drove me home to my uncle's. Just the two of us sitting in the car, driving up the same big street I'd walked down only a few hours earlier. How could everything have changed, my whole life, in so brief a time?

"Is this your car?" I said.

"My dad's."

"It smells new. Is it new?"

"Is what new?" he said.

"The car. Is it a new car?"

"I think it is."

"I like the smell of a new car," I said.

We drove over the train yards, up through Chinatown, the moon in the rear-view mirror. A streetcar rattled by, empty now.

"Hard to believe it's already August," I said. I don't think Bill found much of anything hard to believe. But he nodded cooperatively. He took his right hand off the wheel and rested it on the seat between us. His "petting" hand, it occurred to me.

"I always like the idea of summer," I said. "But somehow it always ends up sort of a disappointment."

Pulling to a graceful stop in front of my uncle's house, Bill turned his handsome, almost feminine features to me. Even in the light from the street lamps, I could see the splash of blood in his cheeks. (*My* blood, it seemed to me.)

"I'm sorry about all this," he said. And in his way, he was. I got out of the car, ran up the flagstone steps, made a small theatrical production of looking for my key, but when I turned to wave I could see from his face in the car window that he understood exactly how I felt but that in five minutes he wouldn't be thinking about it anymore. On his way, no doubt, to Clarissa's house. Her parents, she'd mentioned earlier, were at a film festival in San Sebastian.

When I awoke in the morning, birds chirping outside my window, the room bathed in yellow sunlight (the wrong kind, the too-early kind), I hovered for a second the way you do, on the verge of remembering: a corpse you can almost make out in the mud. Oh yes, *that*. A foul taste in my mouth, my head aching from the beer as if I had an arrow clean through both temples. My girlfriend gone.

I tried to get back to sleep, but like a diver with an air pocket in his suit *(she's gone!)* I couldn't get back under the surface. (How awful it is, more than forty years later, to recall those moments.)

I lay for I don't know how long staring at a crack in the ceiling over my head, a long, lightning-shaped crack, the kind you see over a lake in the summer. And the events of the previous evening, the girl in the red sweater, the Ferris wheel, Bill Cardelle looking down at his loafers, seemed, at the same time, nightmarish *and* inevitable. As if a handful of cards had been thrown in the air and come down in their precise numerical order. While I was lying there, too stunned to do much except stare at the crack in the ceiling and plan to go downstairs to brush my teeth but unwilling to leave my bed, as if by my moving, and with that movement officially beginning the day, the situation would only become *realer*, I heard, for the first time since I arrived at my uncle's, a knock on my bedroom door.

"Yes?"

The door opened, my father came in, and the horror of everything, the unfairness of it, tumbled over me like a stack of wooden chairs. I'd forgotten: fresh from the hospital, determined to make up for "lost time" and "bad behaviour," he had made a plan to take me clothes shopping for the new school year.

In his little blue Morris, we drove uptown, passing on the way the deep ravine on the other side of which I could see Clarissa's white apartment building where, I imagined, in her parents' giant white bed, the silk curtains stirring just so (like the hair on Bill's forehead), the two of them, Clarissa and a boy with blood on his cheeks, stirred, side by side, in their sleep.

I watched the ravine retreat in the mirror and we turned onto Eglinton, still too bright in that awful summer sunshine, and went into Beatty's Store for Young Gentlemen.

It was a day that went on forever. Perhaps, to this day even, the longest of my life. My father, shaky like all alcoholics about their "former" behaviour, asked me questions as if reading from a manual. My answers barely interested him, except for one. "I hear that you have a beautiful girlfriend."

We bought a blazer, which had to be fitted, grey flannels, which had to be measured, button-down shirts, a belt, a house tie, a school tie, gym socks, dress socks; it went on and on and on; at one point, excusing myself to try on a sleeveless grey sweater, I went into the dressing room, closed the door, sat down with my back to the mirror, and wept into my hand.

Two weeks later, I went into boarding in the same squat brick building I now stood in front of. A boarder! One of *those* guys, along with the chronic masturbators and pimple squeezers and unloved children whose parents plied the civil service in Nairobi or Senegal or

East Timor. Those dandruffy, never-have-a-date, sad sack pooches you saw doing their homework on a Friday night! All my life, all my friends, we were "day boys," we went home after school, we took off our ties, we watched television, we slept in on Saturday mornings and we never went to church. But that, too, was gone now. My parents (could they have made a worse decision?) sold our house in the city, other people lived there now, and moved up to our summer cottage. "Less stimulation," my father's doctor recommended. Well, everyone got that.

I shared a room with a boy no one else wanted to room with, whose skin was white as cream and who enjoyed prancing around the room stark naked, flexing his muscles and emitting whoops of laughter. He also had an enormous, uncircumcised unit; it looked like a giant worm and I had an uncomfortable sensation that he found his own nakedness arousing. The window over my bed looked out onto the courtyard and a gloomy statue—the courtyard where I now stood decades later.

A little chamber of horrors, it was. I nearly went mad from the bewilderment of it all. I couldn't get over the notion: when I went up the Ferris wheel, I had a girlfriend; when I came down, I didn't. How could this be? What kind of a world was it where things like this could occur? What are human beings really like? Is language simply a disguise, a way to keep people off the scent of who you really are and what you really want?

After lights out, I took out my little plastic viewer and put it to my eye and pushed down on the button—and there we were.

There we were.

I ran away in the middle of the next night. I slipped out the window into the courtyard and scampered past the statue into the shadows.

It took me all night to hitchhike to the American border crossing. By then the sun had come up; cars streamed by in the brilliant sunlight.

"Where are you going today?" the customs agent said at the mouth of the bridge.

"Niagara Falls," I said.

"For how long?"

"Just the day."

"Why aren't you in school today?"

"It's a scholars' holiday. Do you want to see my student card?"

"Not particularly," he said, amused by his own dryness. "Away you go."

I walked twenty-five, fifty, a hundred yards along the bridge; I looked down at the river crashing below me; the wind picked up; it blew my hair on end. I was seized with the desire to start running, to run and run and run. All my life I had had the suspicion that I was a bad boy and that I was going to be punished for it, that one day a kind of giant fly swatter was going to come down on me with a terrible *whap*. And now here I was, being truly bad, mid-way across the bridge, a rule breaker of the first order, a middle finger extended to law and order and . . . and nothing. There *was* no fly swatter. No God, no hell, no punishment. Nobody even paying attention, much less punishing. A blind man came tapping his way along the bridge toward me, heading to the Canadian side, his black suit flapping in the high wind from the river. I waited till he got past me and then I broke into a run. I ran all the way across the bridge and when I landed at the very end, when I stepped onto an American sidewalk, I swear I was a different boy than the one who had started on the other side.

The sun had set now behind the school's clock tower, its round face slowly yellowing. The door to my old dormitory burst open, and a crowd of teenage boys spilled raggedly out into the courtyard. They looked at me quickly—I could have been a pole or a bicycle rack—and hurried across the flagstones. It must have been dinner-time. I waited till the last one had gone up the steps and into the building; from where I stood, you could hear them moving down the hallway toward the dining room, those high, excited voices.

I looked again at the window of my old room. The student who lived there must have turned off the light and I could see only my reflection in the window.

I lingered in the growing darkness a little longer. There was something more I wanted; there always is. I was trying to imagine what I might have thought that night as I slipped into the October darkness, running from shadow to shadow, running across playing fields and bridges, what would I have *said* if someone had told me that one night many, many years later, when my hair was grey, when I was older than the teachers who teach here (strange notion), that I'd end up back in this courtyard.

And why, I'm not sure, but leaving the school property (I could see two paunchy old boys heffing around the track), I felt a great tenderness for that young boy darting into the night. I found myself thinking that he was, above all else, more than reckless, more than daring, more than naive, something *more*. Some extraordinary quality that I no longer possess. The lack of which, when you think about it, is probably a good thing at my age.

And who would have believed it—that Clarissa Bentley would be my great liberator? The dispeller of superstition. A cruel little girl who grew up to be a dishonest adult but who, more than my mother who adored me, more than an English teacher who inspired me, gave me the rule breaker's freedom for life. A blessing from a monster.

2

Everything Frightened Him

When I was twelve years old, my father, then a successful stockbroker, bought me a gun. It was a .22 rifle with a mahogany stock and a short barrel. He taught me how to use it; how to negotiate a farmer's field, how to climb over a fence without putting a hole in my forehead. It was a small gun, but it could kill, I learned that from the beginning. Imagine then his extreme displeasure when my teenage brother, Dean, shot out half the windows on the ground floor of our country house while my parents were in the city one weekend for a funeral.

I was innocent, of course; even I had the brains not to point a gun at a window and pull the trigger. Especially when it was your *own* house and your parents were coming home the next day. Still, I didn't snitch and took the blame along with him, although now at the age of sixty, having raised two children myself, I cannot imagine why.

Perhaps I thought I was in a movie. I often did during those early years. *Beau Geste*, maybe, the 1939 melodrama where a young Gary Cooper confesses to a crime of which he's innocent—the theft of a valuable jewel—and joins the French Foreign Legion where he dies a hero's death. Exactly my kind of story.

The punishment for the shot-out windows was somewhat less compelling. Instead of sending Dean to a psychiatrist, my parents instructed us to learn Edgar Allan Poe's "The Raven" by heart (my mother's idea), which was a snap for me because I had a magpie's memory and I rather fancied the poem. For Dean, though, it was a struggle, as everything was.

We returned to the city at the end of that summer for school, and the rifle was left behind in a cupboard along with my father's top hat, spare golf shoes, a box of tie pins, and an exotic pair of red dice he'd picked up in Cuba as a single man.

I grew explosively that year, almost six inches (I looked like a prehistoric bird), so by the time the family car rolled down the driveway in a plume of dust and scattered stones the following June, the gun was too little for me. It made me look as though I were playing with a toy. So it stayed in the cupboard.

A few years later, while attending a new boarding school, this one tucked into the countryside, I was caught smoking hashish with a priest, who, as bad luck would have it, lived in a Jesuit retreat just down the road. I was suspended for a week and sent home to our summer cottage, where my father was living alone, my mother having temporarily left him.

But I didn't go straight home. I was afraid to confront him (I'd run away from boarding school the year before), so instead I went to see a dirty, sexy, hair-under-her-arms girl who lived in a rooming house in the student ghetto in Toronto. She came to the door dressed all in black. A stick of strawberry incense glowed in the dark behind her. She said, "Come in."

Sometime that afternoon, my roommate, having guessed where I'd gone, phoned me at the girl's house. "You better do something. They're going to call the police," he said.

I got to the house in Grassmere near midnight. A taxi drove me in from town. The driver, a friendly guy, double-chinned in a red hunter's hat, dropped me off at the side of the road. Too much snow, he said, didn't want to get stuck. I started down the driveway just like I used to after a summer dance, the moon sinister between the tree branches. There was no sound, only my boots in the snow and the river rushing in the darkness to my left.

I came around the bend in the driveway, and below me, a hundred yards from where I stood, I could see our house and behind it the frozen lake, which looked grey in the moonlight. A small lamp glowed in the living room window; the rest of the house was cast in darkness.

I went through the garage with its smell of cold, ignored things and in through the side door. I took off my boots; I peeked in the living room. My father was asleep in an armchair in the corner, a James Bond novel on the table beside him. Sean Connery in *From Russia with Love*.

Hearing me come in, he stirred and woke up. A cleft of grey hair stood straight up on his head; he must have run his fingers through his hair before he fell asleep and it stayed there.

"I didn't think you were coming," he said, and in the mildness of his response, its aura of almost gratitude, our roles changed forever. Or what was left of forever.

Nobody saw his final violent moments, but I have thought about them for many years now. Over and over again, like a movie, each "take" slightly different from the previous one. But all ending in the same place.

This much I know. I stayed with him in that country house for three days. Just the two of us. No sound except the ice falling in the forest, the crows cawing across the field. A lonesome sound. The dark trees in the ravine, tufts of grass poking through the snow, all of it like a black and white painting.

The subject of my suspension never came up; I suppose he didn't want to know the details. Perhaps none of it mattered by then. I asked him if he'd heard from Mother.

He said no, which wasn't true because later the police found a letter from her, from Florida, on the mantelpiece. She was staying in a pink hotel by the sea, the water was warm this time of year, but she was having second thoughts. It was hard, she wrote, to find a "gent" like him. "You are a rare find." She was going to come back after all. Things could be different . . .

But to me, he said no, he hadn't heard from her, and lapsed into silence. I think it was the first time I ever noticed that silence was something you could hear. And then you'd hear the crows again.

What did we do in that rambling house? We played cribbage; we put logs on the fire; we had a bacon sandwich for lunch; I played him that strange Beatles instrumental "Flying." But the electric shock treatment had made him unsure of himself, and while it played, you could see him thinking how he should *seem*.

"Do you like it?" I said.

He nodded. But the song with its dreamy rhythms was assuming a presence in the room and that presence stood between us. As if, along with my suspension, my not coming straight home in its wake, my skeletal, unathletic body, my Beatle haircut, my expulsion the year before, I was presenting him with a numbing checklist of the miles and miles I had moved away from being the son he had always imagined, had wanted me to be. But it was also, he knew, too late and too tiring to complain.

Affectless. I think he felt affectless, which nourished in me cautious stirrings of adulthood. "I'm not afraid of him anymore," I thought. And he sensed it, he heard it in my voice, he saw it in my quick movements, and it must have made him a little frightened of me. All that youth. That glib, indefatigable, got-an-answer-for-everything youth. How exhausting I must have been that weekend.

We went to a ski chalet nearby and sat drinking hot chocolate and watched the skiers slalom soundlessly down the hill. He wore a strange hat, I remember, with giant earmuffs on it, a hat that didn't suit him at all and that, in other times, he would never have worn. He was quite the spiffy dresser, my dad, very old school. Blazers, crisp shirts, cufflinks, club tie, the whole business. But not that weekend. That weekend he gave up.

So three days passed; and early on a grey afternoon he drove me to the train station in town. We waited in the car, the tracks in front of us, the little station house off to the left, and behind it the lake, white and frozen all the way to the opposite shore, a dirty line on the horizon. I asked about Dean, if he'd been up to visit. No. He started to explain, university, a new girlfriend, but ran out of steam before he got to the end of it.

"What are you going to do now?" I said.

He said, "I have to go to the city. I wish I didn't." He touched his fingers to a small cancer scab on his forehead, benign, but it needed removing. No big deal: into the car, an easy drive, stay in the Royal York Hotel, see the doctor in the morning; a drop or two of local anaesthetic, then back to the white house in the country. Done.

But everything frightened him. Even going to the city.

My train pulled away. I headed down the line and didn't give him another thought, not for days. I was seventeen, I thought of nothing for very long except what I wanted. The girl with the hair under her arms. I wanted another night with her and the incense and the Buddha candles.

Later that afternoon, the train a hundred miles away, my mother having a martini in the bar of her Florida hotel, thinking about coming back, how hard it was to find a "gent" like him, my father, John Patterson Monday, packed a small suitcase. A hairbrush, a couple of Oxford shirts, subdued tie, socks, shaving kit. He must have packed it just after he dropped me off at the station. It was getting winter-dark already, the gloom settling around the big house. He put on his raincoat and his hat; he poured himself a belt of Scotch. He was, I guess, just on the verge of calling a taxi from the town when he changed his mind. He rose to his feet, raincoat still on, went into his bedroom and pushed aside his old military uniform that hung from a hanger and selected my .22-calibre rifle, probably because of its short barrel. He went into the living room and opened the drawer of the Queen Anne desk that sat by his armchair and extracted a single, hornet-sized bullet from a box of shells.

Then he returned to the kitchen, sat down at the table, opened the breech of the rifle, put the bullet in the chamber, snapped shut the breech, pulled back the hammer with his long fingers, and, still wearing his hat, put the gun to his temple and fired.

I don't know how long he lay there in the gathering darkness on that kitchen floor, but I know he didn't die right away. You can't, not with a small-calibre gun like that.

It took people three days to find him. Finally the custodian who lived up the road broke a window and came in through the kitchen.

Sometimes I wonder if my father, as he swept the gun up and placed the barrel to his temple, had, in the moment before he squeezed the trigger and the bullet knocked him onto the floor, second thoughts. Did he think it would hurt? Did he think about me? Could he see the ceiling of the kitchen when he hit the floor? Did he know, lying there, that he was dying? Did he regret it? Do you go on dreaming when you die like that, the images moving further and further and further away? Is that what he thought at the very last second: *This is the perfect order of things.*

There is a peculiar addendum to this story. A year or so after his death, I started university in Toronto and I used to tell the pretty girls in the coffee shop that my dad killed himself. I told Raissa Shestatsky one fall afternoon and waited for the smile to fall from her face. Which it did. I figured it made me more interesting, more like a real writer than other people's life stories made them look. I did it for quite a while until one day, while I was telling the story, I saw a picture of my father listening to me, just sitting there, listening; and I was covered in shame. I thought, I have to quit doing this. And I did. And that was that for a long time.

But about ten years ago, something surprising and quite repulsive happened. I received a postcard from Vancouver, three thousand miles away. A colour photograph of the city shot from the air, the harbour bristling with sailboats and launches, high-rises along the waterfront gleaming like jewels in the sunset. Generic stuff. On the back, however, were these words.

> *Darling, I just finished your latest novel which was okay but what I'm really looking forward to is the autobiography of you, your father and the kitchen table. Blood stains and all! Now that would make a movie even David Cronenberg would be interested in, n'est-ce pas?*
>
> *Toodles!*

The card was addressed to my publisher, the signature deliberately illegible.

For reasons I don't entirely understand, I have kept this card and am, at this very moment, looking at its neat, printed script. He—I know it's a man—may be a painter, an illustrator, an artist of some kind. It's that kind of penmanship. But why have I kept it? Am I waiting to match up the handwriting someday? I am. I have unpleasant plans for the person who sent me that card. And I'm prepared to be patient about it.

I have a theory, though. It occurred to me out of the blue one morning while I was taking plates out of the dishwasher. I think that the author of the card, this creature in Vancouver, went to university with me, that he was sitting nearby, maybe even at the next table, when I was telling Raissa or some other girl the "sad" story of my father's death and he overheard it.

And now *this*.

But to get back to my original question: No, I don't think my father died wondering if he was making a mistake. It changes, but these days, now that I'm the same age he was when he died, I don't imagine he was thinking about much in those last moments except getting the job done. It was all a sweep from the moment he pulled back the hammer to the moment the barrel touched the skin on his temple. It's an odd thing, especially for a man who drank a lot, that he didn't finish his Scotch. I've always quietly admired him for that. Courageous, right at the end.

I always think about it, the glass of Scotch on the kitchen table, when I hear "Flying."

Last winter, I was adrift downtown in that dead zone between Christmas and New Year's Eve. Sometime before dark I found myself standing in front of the bus station to which I had fled from boarding school that night in 1966. I stepped around a dirty snowbank and went into the station and bought a bus ticket to our old country house in Grassmere. I had not been back for many years and I was hungry to see the place.

It was lucky timing because not half an hour later we pulled out of the station and swung onto University Avenue. How odd to see your own city through the green-tinted glass of a bus: a street corner where you quarrelled with a girlfriend, a parkette where you ate a hot dog with your children, a doughnut shop where you waited for your laundry to dry, the deserted soccer field of your old high school. Like a tourist visiting your own life.

The bus picked up speed. Malls, giant box stores, warehouses, hydro towers whizzed by. A jet descended in slow motion overhead. Moving beyond the city limits, we gathered speed and rushed along a brown, wet highway. Flat fields on either side. The sun sulking in the clouds. Bulrushes poking through the snow. A farmhouse the colour of dried blood. A straight side road leading nowhere.

Gradually the terrain roughened into cottage country; snow-covered lakes, giant slabs of rock; roadside restaurants shut up till spring, motels with unshovelled parking lots. More snow now. Trees with drooping branches, like children with tired arms.

But right after Orillia the sun broke through the clouds and transformed the countryside, as it does in the Caribbean, into a place of almost romantic possibility. A moose appeared at the edge of the forest, steam rose from the highway; the lakes dotted now with ice-fishing huts; a solitary black figure making his way to shore.

It was nearly four-thirty in the afternoon when the bus pulled off the main highway and drove slowly into town. I got out at the Empire Hotel and, as if sleepwalking, crossed the main street, going up past the movie theatre, then a card shop, till I got to Edwards' Taxi. I went into the office and said I wanted to go out to Grassmere, "If it's still called Grassmere," I added.

"It sure is," the dispatcher said. A friendly, small-town face I almost recognized. "Out by Pen Lake?"

"That's the one."

"What's the address?"

"I don't know. It didn't have an address last time I was there."

"Well, whose house is it?"

"I don't know the name of the people. I haven't been here for a long time. I'm looking for the old Monday place," I said.

"My father used to drive you out there," the dispatcher said offhandedly. "Earl Edwards, my dad."

I recognized him. "Tommy?" I said. He was a plump boy even back then working at the marina, always wiping his hands with a rag and talking like a cowboy. "I remember your dad," I said. And I did, an older version of Tommy's face under a red hunting hat. "He drove me out there . . ." I was going to say when, but I didn't want to start that conversation. ". . . often."

"He passed, oh, fifteen years ago now."

"I'm sorry to hear that."

"Hang on, I'll run you out there myself." Putting on a big winter jacket, Tommy said, "We used to gas up your boat for you, you and your brother. You fellows used to come charging up to the dock and hop out of the boat and say, 'Charge that to Mr. J.P. Monday.'"

I searched his face for a tick of malice, but there wasn't one. "You must have thought we were spoilt little pricks," I said softly.

"Well," he said, glad for *me* to have said it, "that was a long time ago. Lot of water under the bridge." I could see the little boy Tommy again, rubbing his hands with a rag.

"You've got an excellent memory, Tommy."

"I can't remember what happened yesterday if my god-damn *life* depended on it. Ask me what happened twenty years ago, I won't shut up till supper."

It was dark by the time we travelled the five miles out to the house. I wanted to be alone for this part, so I asked him to leave me at the top of the driveway. When I got out of the car, it hit me, that wild, fresh country air.

"You want me to wait?"

"No, I'll be okay."

Tommy considered that for a second. "You remember that Sharon Beilhartz girl? Her father owned the shoe store?"

"Yes."

"You used to go with her."

"Yes, I did. For a summer."

"Well, she's the mayor now. So you better watch your step."

"Nice to see you, Tommy."

I started down the driveway, the river crashing in the ravine on my left, louder than I remembered, the trees bare, taller and overgrown; a scuttling moon. The weather was changing. I turned the bend. The fence post was still there and it seemed that I could hear the Beatles' "Flying" start up in my head. There was a light on in my old bedroom on the second floor. A motion-sensor light sprang on. An expensive city car sat in the garage. They had money, whoever they were.

I knocked on the door. There was no response, and as I knocked again, I could feel my pulse quickening as though I were breaking the law, as though a sour face might yank up the window and say, "You have no business here!"

I thought of going around the back of the house, but this nagging sensation that I was doing the wrong thing stopped me. I was about to head back up the driveway when the front door opened. The same door I'd crashed out of the night I hitchhiked to see Clarissa Bentley. A small, tanned man in a tweed jacket and tie stood in the doorway.

Advancing very slowly—I didn't want to frighten him—I introduced myself.

"Come in," Mr. Keveney said.

And then I went into my old house. It was physically the same place, walls in the same positions, but everything else was different. It danced with colour and freshness, pinks and oranges and bright pastels.

Motioning for me to do likewise, he sat himself down in a corner armchair, precisely where my father's had been. The fire crackled and I began to experience a kind of sleepy vertigo, as though my head were full of feathers.

I detected the vague dusting of an Irish accent in his intro-
duction. The kind of man who puts on a tie for a stay-at-
home Sunday in the country.

I said, "I have an unusual request, Mr. Keveney."

His expression changed, the first hint of suspicion.

"I used to live here," I said.

"When?"

"I left in 1966."

"Who'd you sell it to?"

"I don't know, I'm afraid."

"What was your father's name?"

I told him. He nodded neutrally. I wondered if he
knew. Scanning his large, tanned features—he was no
stranger to mid-winter vacations—I couldn't see any indi-
cation.

"Now tell me," he said, "what is this unusual request?"

"I would like to see my old bedroom."

At that moment a luminous, beautifully dressed older
woman with red hair and a pale face stepped into the living room. Hers was a stronger Irish accent.

"Did you offer him a sherry, Gerald?" she said.

"I don't think I dare," I said. No one found this odd.

Leading the way, they took me up the wooden stairs
and along the narrow hall. Looking into my brother's
bedroom, I saw that it too had been transformed into
bright colours and warm furniture. The bed was stacked

with wrapped presents. "We have a son who lives in Edinburgh and he's coming for a visit with his children," Mrs. Keveney said.

And then we were in my bedroom. The cowboys on the wallpaper were gone. "Lift up the window," Mr. Keveney said.

As my fingers touched the heavy brass latches, I experienced a sensation of absolute familiarity and a strange light-headedness. I looked over at him, puzzled. "Those are the same latches that were there when you were a boy," he said. "We never changed them." I looked down at the latches, at my fingers still under them. So *that's* what Proust meant when he stumbled on the uneven paving stones in Paris and found himself abruptly transported back to Venice where, as a younger man, he had stumbled on a similar set of stairs. That's what he meant by being "beyond time," that you're neither here (in the present in my old country home) nor there (myself as a child lifting a window) but instead in some delicious limbo *in between*. How odd: to come back here to investigate and probe an old wound and, life being life, to come away with something entirely unexpected; in this case, to have finally, after years of missing the point, understood Proust.

"Did that storm window used to rattle in the wind?"

"It did."

"Would you like to see your parents' bedroom now?"

We passed through the kitchen in silence. There was a rectangular pine table pressed against the near wall. It was set for two, one at the end facing the bay window, the other beside it. I looked at the pine table for a long moment, then at the colourful tiles on the floor where the blood had trickled from my father's temple.

And then Mrs. Keveney did the most extraordinary thing. She stepped forward quickly and hugged me, a lovely-smelling, delicately perfumed mother's embrace.

"But where are you staying?" she asked.

"In town."

"No," she said firmly. "You must stay here. Tomorrow you can catch a ride back to town." Outside you could hear the ping of tiny grains of hail hitting the windows. The tick-tock of the grandfather clock in the hallway.

"Perhaps I could have that sherry now," I said.

I stayed downstairs near the fire and talked until my eyes were closing. Then I mounted the stairs and went down the dark hall to my bedroom. I didn't read, I slept immediately. In the night there was a bang in the hallway. I recognized that bang. My mother thought it was poltergeists, but if they were, they were soothing poltergeists and I sank back down into sleep.

I awoke to a glorious morning, the sun pouring down, the lake white and gleaming in the distance. We ate breakfast in the kitchen, toast and scrambled eggs. Delicious. I hadn't eaten for a day.

"You must come back whenever you want. Bring your wife, too. It's a little out of the way up here. We love guests."

And then I started up the driveway, the sun bright overhead. I paused at the post and took a last look. The images of my brother listening to baseball on his radio, Mother dancing in the kitchen with her shirt knotted at the waist, my father with that funny hat, all these images flickered through my memory, so clear, almost touchable. And I suspected that because I could now return to the house whenever I wanted to—I never would. This place inhabited now by such warmth, such friendly souls.

I walked for a few miles through the colourless countryside and then I'd had enough. There wasn't anything more to think about. An empty ice truck drove me the rest of the way to town.

3

"You don't know me, Mr. De Niro, but . . ."

"The best thing about being successful," a friend once told me, "is that you get to tell everybody to fuck off." He told me this at a low point in his acting career, shortly before he gave up the business entirely and married a rich woman. We don't see each other anymore (these things happen), but I have often remembered those words and for a while, quite a *long* while, I believed them: that one of life's great pleasures lies in giving the bird to people and places where you were once a flop. Fuck you, Mary-Lou, and so on.

But with the greying of my hair I have discovered that it's a little more complicated than that. For example, it's not a question of convincing "those people" that they were wrong about you, it's a question, really, of convincing yourself, of convincing, to be more precise, your *body*. Your body remembers failures more easily than success.

I don't know why that is, but it does. And when you put it—your body—back in the same physical places where it once wilted, where it once suffered blows to the heart and blows to the vanity, sometimes, most of the time actually, your body forgets all the things that have happened in the interim and thinks the bad old days are still here.

Which can make going back to arenas of early unhappiness more of a minefield than you might suspect.

When I was twenty-two years old, my mother died during a dinner party in Mexico City. She was making a toast and tumbled off her chair onto the carpet. Someone stole a pearl necklace from around her neck before the ambulance arrived, but apart from that, I'm told the company that evening was pretty good. A few days later I went down to the offices of Nathan and Nathan and, in the company of my brother, Dean, signed some papers.

Thus began my short life as a rich boy. I'm not sure, looking back on the years that followed, how things could have taken a worse, a more destructive turn than that inheritance. It allowed me—or so I thought—to *not* do the one thing that would have made me happy. To work. To get my head out of my rear end and *do* something. But I didn't know that then and I blamed my unhappiness on other things: the search for love, unpublished poetry, the silence of God, cigarettes, cruelty to animals, ugly people, the way my street looked when the sun went behind a cloud.

While friends were going to law school or taking acting classes or apprenticing as journalists or practising the violin or studying for a masters in volcanology, I drifted around an inherited farmhouse in a dressing gown, sleeping till five in the afternoon and occasionally trying to strangle my girlfriend, a German princess with a lisp, the victim of a parent murder-suicide. Between us, three out of our four parents had died by bullets. How could we fail as a couple?

Once, en route to Frankfurt, a few Bloody Marys and two or three sleeping pills convinced me to present myself to my fellow passengers as a professional pool player touring the world. Somewhere over the dark Atlantic, I fell into someone's seat and the plane's steward put me under house arrest at the back of the plane, strapping me like a mummy into the emergency seat. Is there anything more destructive for a young man than unearned income? I think not.

Then, when I was twenty-eight, the year 1978, I married M., a college friend, and a few months later we had an exquisite daughter. M. worked at the Toronto Film Festival (TIFF to insiders) and I used to drop around her office in the afternoons, everyone young and busy. For a while I liked being the boss's "interesting" (read useless) husband. But you can only be "interesting" for so long; after a while, a smell of putrefaction follows you around like a plume. You are out of rhythm with the world. It's a cruel observation, but if you can't *do* something for people, they don't have much time for you. And I had only time.

Little by little it seemed that even the secretaries in M.'s office came to see me as something of a buffoon; so I stopped going around. The light in the office, the noise of busy people, the rattle of typewriters, the excited telephone voices—"I've got Werner Herzog on the line," "Harvey Keitel won't come if that other guy is coming too!" "Can we get some coke for Robbie Robertson?"— set off in my body a sensation of sickening irrelevance. There are few sensations more unpleasant.

When I turned off the light at night, I was aware of something lying on top of me. Failure.

For ten nights in September, the film festival throbbed and dazzled in the heart of Toronto. There were afternoon receptions and industry cocktail parties. Trays of fat shrimp and chilled sauces were ferried through rooms by gorgeous, unemployed actresses. Limousines shuttled back and forth from the airport. Movie stars appeared in local restaurants. There were private dinners for John Cassavetes, Gérard Départdieu, Wim Wenders (for whom I was mistaken on an irritating number of occasions), Richard Gere, Kevin Kline, Agnès Varda, Michael Caine, Jean-Luc Godard, Pauline Kael, Robert Duvall, Jean-

Jacques Beineix, a young Nastassja Kinski (Jesus!), Peter O'Toole, Dennis Hopper, Klaus Maria Brandauer . . . No Woody Allen. Ever. (He knew better.)

There were standing-room-only press conferences at ten in the morning. Translators, agents, producers and the foreign press jostled for seats. Celebrities held forth. They aired their political sensitivities, chortled at each other's jokes, bathed in the false largesse of a man who has just won a prize. Flashbulbs flashed.

There were movies, too, but often they felt merely like a kind of trampoline for puffery and cheek kissing.

People checked into and checked out of the hotels. The lobbies teemed with autograph seekers, photographers, groupies and inconvenienced travelling salesmen. Bacteria accumulated. Print journalists conducted interviews beside the rubber tree in the split-level foyer. Short men in Armani suits and clunky, portable phones hurried along thickly carpeted corridors; sometimes, in the company of an anorexic young woman, they made long-distance calls to Los Angeles and demanded that a script be couriered *immediately*.

Television actors got the smaller rooms. Failed European directors gave seminars so a whole new generation of Canadian directors could learn to fail too.

In front of the cinema houses, the red carpets rolled out, the spotlights whirled, the sidewalks overflowed, television cameras whirred, movie stars exploded from limousines into a blast of light and then were gone inside and everyone left *outside* felt slightly queasy, slightly depressed. But for a few seconds there, you were so close you could almost have touched it.

Sometimes I saw M. in the lobby of a movie theatre with W.C., the festival director. With his bulging forehead and rimless glasses, he was a dead ringer for Joseph Goebbels. Beside him, lanky and hollow-chested, his chief flunky, Billy. Laughing and smoking cigarettes (he had only one lung), he stood too close to people and talked on the "inside." Filling out the trio was a big, carrot-headed lug. He didn't work in the "business," but they gave him hanging-around privileges because he had the curious effect of making everyone feel as though they were doing slightly better with their lives than he was doing with his. Johnny was like Chekhov's Uncle Vanya that way. You may have wanted to be a novelist and ended up writing copy for a children's snowsuit catalogue, you may have seen Bertolucci staring back at you one morning when you looked into the mirror but you're still making industrials on suppository factories, you may have wanted to be a movie star but you're taxiing film cans from the censor to the theatres . . . but no matter your disappointments, you were still doing better—better intellectually, sexually, creatively, aesthetically—than Johnny. That's why everyone liked him.

And what, I wondered, was with those cutesy-pie nick-names, Billy, Johnny and, don't forget, "Weiner" (W.C.'s nickname)? Grown men! Am I being too harsh? Not by a half. It's funny how much I loathed them then and, even in recalling them thirty years later, how vivid my dislike remains.

Sometimes I'd see Billy dancing at a gala ball. He fancied himself light on his feet, a real Motown man. He had all the moves. Sometimes he'd stop and talk to me, standing very close, very confident, his face only inches away; but not for long; he had important places to be. With a flourish, he'd be gone. Hotfooting it across the room to talk to so-and-so. More laughter. More inside stuff. Ho-ho-ho. Ha-ha-ha. I seethed with hatred and wanted them all dead. Just going near the film festival during those ten days made me want to murder people—it was misery about my own professional life, of course, a life that now seemed stillborn—but I couldn't stay away.

There were minor scandals. A Hollywood director ordered eight magnums of Veuve Clicquot and charged them to the festival. A French actor overdosed on cocaine (but not before he'd bored everyone to death); somebody screwed somebody's girlfriend in the bathroom of the hospitality suite. Film prints got lost, turned up at the wrong theatre. A Chinese art film played the midnight horror festival with no subtitles. No one seemed to notice.

During those ten days in Toronto, nerdy men—film critics mostly—came into fashion. Badly dressed, over-weight social cripples ambled through cinema lobbies, often in twos and threes, quiet in their superiority, their "knowing" better than anyone else, so subtle in their con-demnation that it made your heart hammer to tell them you liked something. They didn't tell you you were wrong; they just dropped you into a Rolodex of inferior creatures and returned their attention to each other.

In the midst of all this was my wife, M. Dispatching drivers, issuing directives, making snap decisions, juggling screenings, switching suites to rooms for lesser stars and rooms to suites for bigger stars, scolding theatre man-agers, placating actors, booking boardrooms, firing the recalcitrant, stroking the exhausted, she was a sun at the centre of the universe. Or so it seemed to me, standing on the fringes of that dreadful, light-swept film festival office ("the bunker," they called it). I had, during those ten days, all the vanity of a successful writer but none of the work to substantiate it. Like the young André Gide, I was furious that the world would not credit me for the work I *assumed* I would eventually produce.

Sometimes I saw M. on the street in a buzzing hive of people, always at the side of a star ("It's Dustin Hoffman!") or inside a ring of directors and producers and publicists and writers (the writers trying to maintain their writerly dignity, their above-itness, but just as heart-poundingly excited as a child on Christmas Day).

"Dusty! Dusty! Over here! Over here!"

You couldn't resist it, you could not *not* be affected, you couldn't not feel that somehow you were to the side of life. I suspect now that even the people in "the bunker" felt at the margins of life, that this thing, this "it" was an entity where, even if you spent your life near it, around it, you could still never arrive at its centre, never grab it, hold it, make it yours. Because "it" didn't exist; it wasn't a thing or a place. It was a *non*-place, and you could only be on the outside of it.

Sometimes I went to the evening gala screenings, but, to be honest, the excitement, the focus on *other* people, made me sick. So I knocked around my apartment, gave my daughter, Franny, dinner, bathed her, put her in her pyjamas, read her a story and then . . . and then: it was as if there were a huge suction in the city, it sucked and sucked and sucked, and, like shavings to a magnet, it seemed to draw everyone to it, me included.

Wriggling with discomfort and spurts of aggression and ill will, I opened the door for the babysitter and hurried like a junkie to the festival hospitality suite. It was misty, there was an aura of mystery to the streets. Perhaps tonight was the night. The night that my life began. That things started. What things? "We've had our eye on you, mister, and we think we have a proposition here that just might interest a man of your skills."

How did it happen to me? How did I get there? Poor character? Maybe. Immaturity? Certainly. On those mornings when I woke up, the sun a cold pearl outside my window, my daughter pulling at my blankets, Get up, Daddy, get up, I wondered how, with such a promising start, decent looks, decent brains, a private-school education, free university, okay parents (not enlightened but not sadists, either), I had managed to come up with so little.

That evening, I remember, I got to the hospitality suite a bit early. The gala film was just getting out down by the lakeshore. A bolt of lightning cracked over the lake; fat raindrops spattered against the bay windows. I was at the bar talking to the bartender when M. and an entourage of French producers swept in. She gave me a frosty hello, looked at my half-empty beer glass, asked me one or two questions, hesitated just long enough to let me know, without saying anything, that I'd been drinking and she could hear it in my voice. And then, as I began to explain myself, as I began to make an observation (I was just being friendly) about Éric Rohmer's films (more precisely written than you'd guess), she turned her back and walked away. She did it on purpose, of course, and it left me diminished and reeling. By then we both hated each other.

By two o'clock in the morning, the hospitality suite was noisy and full; a bank of cigarette smoke hung over the room; the talk got louder and louder; even the doorman had a drink in his hand. People waited in the corridor; the door opened, you saw faces of all shapes, hopeful, straining, smiling, irritated, all trying to get inside, trying to get close to something that, they were sure, was just on the other side of the door. A television interviewer with the pushed-in face of a monkey arrived dressed as though he were in a Noël Coward play. He was famous for knowing all the details of a star's life, what he said to his grade six teacher, what the director of a summer-stock play whispered to him between act one and act two all those years ago; he fancied, did Monkey-Man, that it made him the most professional of interviewers; to me it made him a shameless, zipper-licking flunky. With him was a white-haired film critic, Toronto's least persuasive heterosexual, in spite of the three children and the nice wife. (They had an understanding, no doubt.)

They were ushered in; the door closed again. I saw a television actor at the bar; a movie star moved in beside him; they exchanged greetings; you could see the movie star was pretending to take an interest in the television actor's work, but everybody knew, especially the monkey-faced talk-show host who was watching them, transfixed, who was the boss, who was the king. And it was the movie star, his drink served, who moved away first, laughing shrilly and nodding, delighted to get away but not wanting to make an enemy. I stood there a few minutes longer, talking to the television actor. Fifteen years earlier he'd been the biggest star on television, the action hero of an absurd futuristic series where he played half man, half cyborg. Now he was doing a small independent film, surprisingly well written, which he'd produced and starred in. He'd had his day, though, everyone said it, but talking to him at the bar (he talked in an easy Texan accent) I found myself liking him, feeling strangely protective; saying nice things about his acting, how looking effortless was acting's great challenge, which made him offer to buy me a drink (they were free).

And then he was gone, absorbed into the pollen of a young woman who had stood shamelessly at his elbow for our entire conversation. I noticed across the room, like two pistols pointing at me, the small, angry eyes of my wife, M. She'd been drinking; some switch had clicked in her head, and not a good one, either. It had turned the whole room, or rather—and this is the unattractive part— the people she didn't *need* in the room, into a swarm of irritating mosquitoes.

She was giving me "the look." Everyone knew that look by now. The bartender got it if she saw him having a beer; a festival underling got it for interrupting a conversation with Bertolucci's producer (a projectionist had not turned up for the Howard Hawks retrospective). The programmer for the midnight horror festival got it when he inquired if he could take an extra case of beer for his overworked staff. And now me. I'm not sure what the infraction was, but I remember thinking that it wasn't the face of the young girl I had so adored in university, her brown hair falling to each side of her sculpted face. How awful for us to have arrived here.

To avoid her, I went to the far end of the hospitality suite. There was a washroom back there. Standing just to the side of it, his arms folded like a steel turtle who has found himself outside his shell, was Robert De Niro. I'd forgotten he was coming this year. He was slighter than I expected, jeans, a short-sleeved shirt, but nevertheless I recognized the aura around him: it said simply, "Don't." Don't tell me you loved my little joie-de-vivre dance in *Mean Streets* (the exploding mailbox); don't ask me why Martin Scorsese prefers me to Harvey Keitel (that's an easy one; just meet Keitel and you'll know why).

I had almost grasped the doorknob when he moved his wiry, tense frame a few inches over so it was now directly between me and the door. It was subtle, but it was there.

"There's someone in there right now," he said. We exchanged looks. He was in a difficult position. He had begun a conversation that, by habit, he had no desire to continue.

Standing side by side, our arms crossed at the elbows, staring straight ahead, neither of us said anything as the room hummed before us. Billy, W.C.'s lieutenant, popped his head around the corner. He had been chortling it up with a lanky American actor but was taking a short break to confirm that there wasn't somebody more important in the room. When he saw whom I was standing beside (he assumed we were talking), his features, how he felt about me, underwent a dramatic transformation that produced two back-to-back sensations in my body: one, a kind of glowing pleasure, glory by proxy, followed immediately by disgust with myself, a strange hollowing sensation as if I hadn't eaten that day. So it's come to this, I thought. Your life achievement: standing beside a movie star and people mistaking you for his friend. And I again had that sensation of having missed an important train. A train that, when you're young, feels as though it only comes once.

Turning slightly, I said, "Excuse me, Mr. De Niro, you don't know me, but I believe you know my wife, M.?"

"M.?" he said, frowning. (I knew that frown; I'd seen it in *Taxi Driver*.) "M. as in M. *here*? In Toronto?"

"Yes," I said.

He recrossed his arms and shifted his weight, looking straight ahead. A sign the conversation was over.

"She's my wife," I said.

Pause. Then: "M. is your *wife*?" he said. And in that curiosity I heard what I had sometimes suspected those mornings when my eyes opened and I realized sleep, at least for that day, was a subway car I could not get back on. "M.," it implied, "is married to a loser like *you?*"

I felt the floor open under me. Nobody likes me, I thought.

The bathroom door opened and a beefy figure stepped by me, brushing my shoulder, no excuse-me, not anything, just Harvey Keitel pushing into the shadowy room in body language that said, *So?* A few moments later a doe-like young woman with big tits and a tiny brain—she was a festival regular—came out looking as she always did, stupid and desirable.

"Be seeing you," De Niro said, not, of course, because we'd be seeing each other but because, like many movie stars, he didn't want to leave a smouldering campfire behind him. You don't want someone showing up at your office in SoHo with a long memory and a Magnum .357.

I went home with a waitress that night—she had a speech impairment from a failed suicide attempt—and the debacle was complete.

Then, life being life, I won a few hands that I needed to win. It makes me vaguely woozy when I think how much luck had to do with it. I got a job on television talking about movies; it was "bar chat," of course, with the intellectual rigour of a guy with a martini in his hand—except that here the guy with the martini in his hand, so to speak, was on television; and being on television imparts, even to a cretin, a strange legitimacy. I was aware of the fraudulence but of insufficient character to not be delighted by it.

I wrote a few books, none of which sold many copies, but just the *fact* of them, the fact that they existed in the world, even in small numbers and never at the front of the store, made me feel that I had had a decent life, that I hadn't ended up like that "other" guy.

Many years went by.

And then one September night last year, the film festival raging like a forest fire throughout the city, I was in the back of a taxi going to meet friends for dinner. We slowed down in front of a movie theatre. It was a gala night, spotlights swirling on the sidewalk, movie stars descending from limos, and I remembered how awful it all used to make me feel. It struck me with a flush of almost physical excitement that if there was ever a place that called out for a revisit, it was the Toronto Film Festival. What fun to bask in old scars and slights and the knowledge that I had survived them.

I dropped around the festival office the next day. "Weiner," Billy, my ex-wife, M., were all long gone, but I knew the new director, Peter Jensen, a pleasant man with a sourceless English accent. I told Peter that I was writing a novel about the early days of the film festival, would it be okay if I hung around a bit: went to some films, some press conferences, a few parties, just to "get the feel" again. He said yes, of course. His assistant, a little troll whose head was so infected with glamour by proxy that she didn't even bother trying to be nice (successful men are often piloted by these creatures), asked a few frowning questions; but I've dealt with assholes before and the meeting ended on a co-operative note and a handful of passes and party invitations.

Remember the light-swept office? All those busy young people, typewriters clacking, phones humming, Martin Scorsese on hold? The typewriters were gone, but everything else was the same. I recognized a frizzy-haired woman from a small northern town (grey-haired and shawled now) and went over to her desk. We chatted for a bit, but after only a few minutes I began to feel an odd sensation, as if I was boring her or keeping her from something, and I thought, this is how I *used* to feel in this office. A sensation of irrelevance. But that had been almost twenty-five years ago. I looked closely at the woman's face. She didn't *seem* bored; no, the problem was me, was *in* me, as if some old poison, locked away now for years in a special film festival bottle, were slowly leaking into my body from a crack in the cork.

I found myself trotting out a rather shopworn anecdote about interviewing George Harrison in London, and with each theatrical pause I felt myself sinking deeper and deeper. And again I asked myself, why are you feeling this? And why are you behaving like this, currying the favour of a woman you barely know and never gave a shit about in the first place? And yet I could not talk out the sensation. The lights, the busy chatter, the ringing of telephones had set it off. It was as if inside their zone I was a kind of prisoner.

I didn't stay long, and as the elevator sank downwards, as I passed through the lobby and out into the soft September sunshine, as I began to make my way down a narrow side street, I felt the grasp of these awful feelings lessen its grip, like a belt being slowly loosened around my chest. What, I wondered, was *that* all about? But I knew what it was about, and the notion that it had even happened felt like a defeat, as if this violent response was a personal shortcoming, the *proof* of a shortcoming.

I went back again that night. I went to the world premiere of a new American film. The director, writer, producers and actors all paraded on stage. A glittering audience applauded with a wave of almost holy excitement as the star, a baby-faced actor in a white suit, told a story about the last time he was in Toronto, about a customs official who'd said, "I'm a big fan!" and then asked him for ID. Waves of sympathetic laughter. What a dunce! Asking for ID, can you believe it?

There was a brief question-and-answer. What drew you to the material, tell us something funny that happened on set, do Oscar nominations really matter?

And there it was again, this feeling of being slowly poisoned, of being excluded from something; that the centre of life was elsewhere, up on that stage, and that I, along with all the other anonymous people in the audience, was stuck in the marshes, the shallows.

But how, I wondered, could you be distressed to be on the margins of something that you were no longer interested in being on the inside of? I began to see myself as a sort of comic figure, a collection of uncontrollable nervous twitches and responses over which I, their ostensible owner, had almost no control. And what did that imply? That there were some experiences simply too big to wipe out, to neutralize? But we're not talking about a madhouse or a prison or a torture chamber. We're talking about a fucking film festival.

All night long I wandered about in a toxic fog. I took a taxi to the post-gala screening down at the waterfront, hundreds of beautiful young men and women dressed to the nines, all talking, all thrilled to be there. I drifted among them like a ghost and then, when I got to the end of the room, I turned around and started back through the crowd again. I knew lots of people. I shook hands, I joked, but I had the feeling that they were keeping me from something, that there was some other place in the room I should be, some other conversation I should be having.

And all night long, it seemed, I was circling the hospitality suite on the twenty-sixth floor of the Hyatt Plaza. Knowing what was going to happen there (more of the same), I still felt compelled to go, like rubbing your tongue against a chipped tooth. But it infuriated me: to be at the mercy of such irrational, unpleasant feelings after so many years, after a decent life and lovely children, to be returned here, to this hungry, diminished state.

I saw Weiner in a clutch of local politicians and arts bureaucrats. Weiner, an older Joseph Goebbels now, thin as a rake. (Someone told me he'd taken up long-distance running, the final domain of the sexless life.) He was with his flunky, Billy, still standing too close to people. (Johnny had died in the interim of testicular cancer.)

I went over; they were talking about an actor's performance, how "over the top" it was. They both laughed, stealing glances at each other and laughing some more. They caught sight of me. Their faces hardened with politeness. We talked for a moment; wrong word; you don't *talk* to guys like that, you banter. We bantered for a moment, but was it just my imagination or did Weiner turn away from my conversation before its point of logical extinction? Did he turn away a hair too quickly (this man whom I didn't even like) to address an observation to Billy that the script for Tuesday afternoon's film was a "hair-over-the-bald-spot script"? An observation with which Billy chuckled his agreement with a shake of the head that said, "It's all so *transparent!*"

And then they were gone and I stood in the gathering late-night crowd, the lights lowered, the volume of voices rising, the illuminated city on display outside the picture window where once, I remembered, it had rained.

Then I saw my daughter. How beautiful she looked in her party dress with her three best friends. They blew into the room with such freshness, you could hear their laughter from where I stood. And just *seeing* her triggered something in me. An instinct for survival. I don't belong here, I thought, and then I realized that it didn't matter *why* I didn't belong, that it was not something to fix but rather something to act on. When the backs of these beautiful young women were turned to order drinks from the bar, amidst shrieks of surprise and youth, I stole out the door I came in. I hurried along the hall in case she'd seen me. And for the second time that day I could feel the stranglehold of my past, of my body's response to it, loosen around my chest. I hurried through the lobby. I saw M. standing by the elevator. She was with Catherine, my son's mother. My two ex-wives going for a drink together in the hospitality suite. In a world where such a gorgeous, civilized thing could happen, there was, again, only one conclusion to be drawn: The ugliness was in me. Not at the film festival.

And as I broke out onto the street, the fresh September air hitting me in the face, as I sped along the sidewalk, I felt things dropping away from me, you could almost hear them, like an old car shedding its unnecessary parts.

Your past really is a country where you used to live. You can't not have been there, but you can sure as hell not go back for a visit. And as I moved further away from the throbbing jewel on the twenty-sixth floor of the Hyatt Plaza ("She's married to *you*?"), breaking through a wave of late-night partiers coming from the opposite direction, I began to feel better and lighter. Because I had, at last, actually *learned* something, a small strategy that, this time, might even stick. So simple, too: if a place makes you feel bad, don't keep going back.

So here's how the story ends. I left a message on my daughter's voice mail when I got home. I said I had a bunch of party passes and film tickets for her. Exactly a year later, festival time again, I was driving my eleven-year-old step-daughter home from a birthday party (there were boys this year). I took my usual route along Bloor Street. We passed a movie theatre; there was a crowd gathering on the sidewalk. A camera crew interviewing a bearded young man. A young man on top of the world in a way he may never be again; people were reaching over the red ropes calling his name, and it's true, I still felt that slightly sickening pull; I always will. But I didn't look away. I rolled down the window, I let my gaze rest on the people, on their excited faces, on their hands reaching over the ropes; and then the traffic light changed, the intersection cleared, and the car ahead of me moved forward into the evening.

4

The House with the Broken Spine

When I think about myself as a young man, I picture a large, dishevelled bird, the kind that flies into the house, knocks over lamps, disturbs people at their meal and then, after a few destructive spins around the room, shoots back out the window. Of course, that's not how I appeared to me *then*. Then I entertained (and not always privately) the idea that my life was a novel, that "people" watched my trajectory with head-shaking admiration. *What's he up to next?* It makes me blush to say all this because the truth, as we all know, is that, apart from my arrivals and exits, no one thought about me very much at all.

Oddly enough, as the years have gone by, it seems that life *itself*, not I, has come to resemble a novel. Characters appear and disappear, resurfacing later in the story in a way that often beats the pants off fiction. When *War and Peace* appeared in 1862, Tolstoy's sisters were outraged to find verbatim transcripts of their dinner-table conversation. His response: a shrug. If you don't want to read about yourself, don't have dinner with a writer.

Speaking of *War and Peace*, do you remember Justin Strawbridge, the boy who took me to the Place Pigalle the day of my execution at the hands of Clarissa Bentley? You do? Well, this'll surprise you. It sure surprised the hell out of me.

Almost a year after the visit to my old boarding school dormitory, my wife, Rachel, and I, having spent a bickerish week or two, decided to take a holiday together. And this holiday, it turned out, provided me with a chance, however unwitting, for another "return."

We didn't plan on going too far away. Just enough of a habit breaker to clear off the barnacles that grow on any married couple if they don't pay attention. So we booked a splashy, overpriced room at a country inn an hour north of the city. We couldn't really afford it—it had been an expensive summer (new roof, broken water pipe, unemployed children)—but we couldn't afford new spouses, either. So it was an easy decision. And it worked. We went for walks in a dark forest, rented a canoe for the afternoon, played pool in the guest room, ate a fabulous dinner, drank a second bottle of wine back in the room, fooled around in our jammies, and then, with the river rushing below our window, slept like logs. By the end of three days we remembered why we'd liked each other in the first place. Coming back to town, even after so short a time, covered the city in a spanking-new coat of paint.

But I see that I'm getting ahead of myself again. On our way out of town, as we left the city behind and moved into the green countryside, I noticed certain things—a red barn, a deserted crossroads, a silo, a descending field—that seemed familiar, albeit distantly. Passing a road sign— Sweet Cherry Lane—I realized I had, in fact, been there before.

You never quite make friends again the way you do in your youth. And later in life, when, for one reason or another, those friendships chip and fade away, they are like a missing tooth. You never replace them. The great friendship of my life—and my life's greatest disappointment—was Justin Strawbridge.

You can't explain why you love someone, why a best friend is a best friend. It always sounds oversold, never quite convincing. Better take the route of the sixteenth-century French philosopher Michel de Montaigne. Talking about the death of his closest friend, he said in one simple, heartbreaking sentence: *"Si l'on me presse de dire pourquoi je l'aimais, je sens que cela ne peut s'exprimer qu'en répondant: parce que c'était lui, parce que c'était moi."* ("If you were to press me to say why I loved him, I can say no more than it was because he was he and I was I.")

In our early twenties, Justin and I had a tiff over a Polish girl (sexy in a consumptive way). She played us both for fools, and we didn't see each other for many wasted years. And then one night more than a decade later, I found myself nostalgically tipsy in a bar and I called him. It took only several seconds to dial the numbers and even as the phone rang, it seemed odd that so simple, so brief a gesture—dialing a number—had kept old friends apart for a decade.

We met a few days later in a dark, sordid strip club downtown. (His idea.) The years had hardened him physically. He looked thin and greasy, hunched over the Formica table, shovelling some kind of salad into his mouth with a too-small plastic fork. He had a room upstairs, over the bar, he told me. Two men passed the table wearing three-quarter-length brown leather jackets. Small-time thugs. He nodded at them. They sat over in the corner and looked at us. One of them said something and the other laughed and I had the uncomfortable feeling they were talking about me, about what a wimp I was. The waitress came over, dollar bills spread between her red-tipped fingers. I ordered a beer; Justin shot the waitress a look, as if just the act of my ordering bothered him.

"Bobby?" she said. She was talking to him. To Justin.

"I'm good," he said. The waitress went over and stood by the bar.

"*Bobby?*" I said.

"That's what they call me down here. Bobby Blue." He said it with a dusting of mildly aggressive pride, as if being called a tough-guy name, however absurd, was, for a rich kid slumming it "down here," some kind of *accomplishment*. Notwithstanding the fact that it makes me nervous when people change their names: there's almost always something wrong with them, a mine shaft right through the middle of their personality. But I pushed the thought away. I didn't want any of that today.

We chatted about this and that, but Justin seemed stiff, rather formal. It was as though, after my phone call, a videotape of the "incident" with the Polish girl (a drunken, late-night visit) had started up in his imagination and his thoughts had taken an unforgiving turn. After a while (me nodding, finishing his sentences, laughing a touch too heartily), I noticed a man standing by the bar, looking this way. I'd seen him on the way in. A weightlifter's body in a black turtleneck sweater and beret.

Justin put down his too-small fork and reached for his coat on the chair behind him.

"Are you *going*?" I said.

It was disgracefully rude, he knew it, and for a second he lost his resolve. "I'm meeting my mother." There it was again, the phony, parent-pleasing frown that I had distrusted even as a child. (It always signalled a betrayal at hand.) Except now he was thirty-five. From the corner of my eye I saw him join the man at the bar. Then Justin

Strawbridge, wearing a long-tailed cowboy coat, disappeared into the bright light of the doorway, the ape in the beret following.

What an absurd coat, I thought. What *could* he be playing at?

But sometimes it's simply too much trouble to stay mad at an old friend, and I suppose that's what happened with us. Again memory fails me, who contacted whom, I don't recall, although I have a feeling it was Justin who phoned. Why, I'm not sure, perhaps a last grasp for a life raft.

Six months later, it was spring now, I found myself riding a motorcycle along a country road, the same Sweet Cherry Lane that I would later notice from the car with my wife. You could smell the warm grass; farms dotted the horizon; the whole world, it seemed, swam in a lush green wind. In my overnight bag was a bottle of Scotch and a well-worn, brick-sized paperback of *War and Peace* (the divine Constance Garnett translation). I wanted to give my old friend a taste of the greatest novel ever written but also a glimpse of what I was like, what pleased me, moved me, delighted me these days. In anticipation, I'd even highlighted certain passages. I imagined a late night, boozy reading: perhaps an excerpt from Nicholas Rostov's flight in the rush of French troops; or Princess Marya Bolkonsky's monologue about love never coming her way—a section so heartbreaking that I'd never read it aloud for fear my throat would tighten and my voice take an embarrassing wobble.

Turning onto a gravel road, I caught sight of Justin Strawbridge waiting in the distance. Behind him, a house with a crooked spine. Crows sat on power lines overhead. Black butterflies flickered among the dandelions. He waved once and then quickly went inside. That was how it began.

We had a great deal of fun that night, those rituals that old friends do when they haven't seen each other for years. You retell stories you both know, and know you both know, revisit old hangovers and old lovers and old disgraceful moments, all in extreme colours now, all agreeably weightless; we touched on "the incident" with the Polish girl and apart from his eyes lingering a moment longer than they should have on my features, the evening moved on. We played songs for each other from albums that no one listened to anymore.

"You know," Justin said, listening for a moment to the Beatles' "All My Loving," "I've never really liked that song. There's something dull right at the heart of it."

"Like an apple. It's boring the way eating an apple is boring," I said.

"Too true."

"It's all promise and no delivery."

"No chorus, either. All the best Beatle songs have a great chorus."

"'I Saw Her Standing There.'"

"'When I Get Home.'"

"Does a hook get any better than the hook in 'When I Get Home'? The Beatles doing Wilson Pickett."

"Unbelievable."

"Absolutely unfucking believable."

"'This Boy.'"

"It *does* get better. 'This Boy's got an even *better* chorus. How could anybody write a chorus that's so fucking great?"

And at this we both laughed in delight, for no apparent reason.

Refreshing his drink in the kitchen, Justin said, "If I asked you to kill my mother, would you help me?"

Pause. "Come again."

"She never liked the Beatles."

"You want to kill your mother because she didn't like the Beatles?"

"No, I want to kill my mother because she's a cunt."

From that point on, the evening only comes back to me in fragments, like an avant-garde film. (It must have been the switch to brandy.) We talked about Walt Whitman (Justin's guy); standing by his library (quite a large, distinguished collection of hardbacks), he read me the final stanzas of *Song of Myself*. I listened with pleasure not because I gave a shit about Whitman (I don't) but because Justin Strawbridge was there, in front of me, my boyhood

friend, and we were at ease with each other again, as if it
had been weeks, not more than a decade. As if a part of
my life which I'd believed lost forever had simply *recom-
menced*. God, how I'd missed him!

He retrieved a manuscript from a mahogany desk—I
had the feeling I'd seen some of this furniture before—and
read me a selection of poems that he'd written himself;
rolling stanzas affecting a sugary reverence for nature, the
godliness in all things living, the circle of seasons, the big
round moon. It was, from beginning to end, bullshit, but I
clapped and called for more.

Then it was my turn. "Here's a little something I came
across while you were away." His eyes settled on me again.
I read him Prince Andrei's thoughts just seconds before a
shell explodes in front of him in the Battle of Austerlitz:

"Can this be death?" Prince Andrei wondered, with
an utterly new, wistful feeling, looking at the grass.
At the wormwood, and at the thread of smoke coiling
from the rotating shell. "I can't die, I don't want to
die, I love life, I love this grass and earth . . ."

I looked up with an expression of anticipation and
found my friend staring into the other room.

"Just a moment," he said, and went quickly into the
kitchen. Sitting there, the book still open in my hands, I felt
a sting of embarrassment, but also a sensation of having

squandered something delicate. And with that came a sudden, unwelcome memory of an incident which had taken place a few years earlier in a bar on the island of Martinique. Lonely and a bit drunk one night, I struck up a conversation with a handful of French sailors—they were on shore leave—and in the course of events, more drinks, the evening getting later and later, I told them I was a "writer"; and to prove it (as if it needed proving) I produced from my shoulder bag a pristine edition of my very first novel, it had just been published, and began to show it around; and one of the sailors yanked the book from my hands and, standing on his tiptoes (the bar was crowded), began to read from the first chapter in a singsong voice with a heavy French accent. I snatched it back, but it was too late; the damage, the "sullying," was done.

Justin came back into the room, animated with relief. "I thought I lost it," he said.

Remembering that night in Martinique (you must protect the precious things in your life), I discreetly closed *War and Peace* and laid it on the table beside my chair. Justin appeared not to notice or, for that matter, to remember what we'd just been doing.

Things moved forward, and near midnight he took me upstairs and showed me a machine gun he'd purchased through the mail. We went onto the second-floor patio. In the distance you could see a single pair of headlights moving across the darkness. A sky of needle-prick stars. The air warm and thicker than in the city, a smell that excites.

Justin went to the end of the patio, shouldered the weapon and fired off a deafening round of automated fire into the lawn below. You could see lumps of grass and earth jumping up like hedgehogs. The air around us turned grey with smoke and the smell of cordite.

"Those cocksuckers," he said.

I woke up the next morning in an airy room on the main floor. Outside my window was the driveway, behind it a field bespeckled with dandelions and daisies. The sun was high in the sky; noon maybe; bees hummed in the eaves-trough. It had been years since I'd drunk hard liquor and when I sat up in bed, it was as though a tray of silverware slid forward inside my head and clanked against the front of my skull. I wondered fleetingly if I might have damaged my brain.

I found Justin in the kitchen. He was seated at the table, chopping up a greyish powder with a razor blade. He looked grim, oddly purposeful.

I picked up my copy of *War and Peace* from the table and was about to return it to my bag when he said, "Not now."

I put it down. After a moment I said, "What's that?"

"TCP."

I said, "What does that stand for?"

He ignored the question.

"Will it work for a hangover?" I asked cheerfully.

A slight, ironic smile. "It'll make you stupider, but it's worth it."

Twenty minutes later, I lay in the dandelion field behind his house. Nauseated, sweating, a sense of iron dread, of a life misspent, clawing at my heart.

"Have I taken something that might kill me?" I said.

Justin sat beside me, chewing nonchalantly on a blade of grass. "What?" he said.

"What is that stuff, that TCP?"

He said, "It wouldn't make any sense if I told you."

I said, "My heart is racing. I'm not going to have a heart attack, am I?"

"I don't think so."

"Should I go to the hospital?"

"It's a glorious day," he said. "You shouldn't be like this. You hold on too tight."

"Just tell me," I said, "please, do I have anything to worry about? Am I going to die from this stuff?"

Turning his pale blue eyes toward me, he said, "You will if you don't pray with me." And then he did the most extraordinary thing. He stripped off his clothes, his shirt, his pants, his underwear, and began a series of obscene somersaults, like a maggot rolling in the dandelions under the bright summer sunlight. It was clear that my childhood friend had gone completely insane.

Kneeling as though in church, he clamped his hands together and began to pray. *"Our Father, Which art in heaven—"*

"What does TCP stand for?" I shouted.

"Hallowed be thy Name. Thy kingdom come . . ."

"Justin! TCP! What does it *mean!*"

He came to a halt. His eyes settled on me again, shattered prisms in a sweaty face. "You should never have fucked her," he said, almost with regret, as if to say, It's too bad all this has to happen to you, but you asked for it.

Then he started back to the house, stark naked, carrying his clothes. "You should never have fucked her," he repeated, not looking back. And in a moment he was gone—into his car and down the driveway, a plume of dust rising behind him. The hum of cicadas rose and fell in the yellow fields.

I went back inside the farmhouse and lay down in the white bedroom. Time passed. The room cooled off; the sky darkened; I got up to go to the bathroom; I drank three glasses of water from a toothbrush glass; I looked out the window; across the dark fields, the city glowed like an icebox.

I was just drifting off, that very second between sleep and wakefulness when your thoughts seem to forget whose they are and, like a herd of frightened deer, take off in their own direction. The sound of a car door slamming woke me up; there were voices and the musical notes of a wind instrument. When I looked out the window, I saw this: a stocky man in a beret tootling on a flute while Justin danced clumsily, like a bear, in the driveway.

I came out onto the porch.

"I want to introduce you to somebody," Justin said.

The man in the beret removed the flute from his full red lips. It was the man I'd seen in the strip club. There was a sudden knocking at my heart. Some people's eyes you know not to look into for too long.

"Duane Hickok," Justin said.

I shook hands with him, avoiding his eyes, frightened that he might smell fear on me, like a dog can. I can't say why he scared me except I sensed that he was capable of a kind of violence the borders of which went well beyond my experience, beyond even my occasional four-in-the-morning revenge fantasies. A man who could kick you in the mouth without an elevation in his pulse. Moreover, I suspected, or rather intuited at an animal level, that you could never be entirely sure what would set it off; a remark, a look, a gesture of "disrespect," you wouldn't know it until he was on you.

I stepped back inside the house and gestured privately to Justin. "You can't let that man in the house," I whispered.

Pale, his breath metallic, Justin rounded his eyes with parent-pleasing surprise. "Why not?"

I don't think I replied, but I felt something fall inside me. I went back into my bedroom, packed up *War and Peace* along with my toothbrush, leaving behind Justin's self-published book of "poetry" (so exuberantly accepted the night before), and soon after started down the darkening driveway, the sound of stones crunching under my motorcycle. Justin, his brow guiltily furrowed, stood on the porch stairs, his hand raised in farewell. (Where had I seen that gesture? Yes, right. *The Great Gatsby*.)

I stopped at the juncture with the main road. Justin and Duane had gone inside; the house was wildly lit up now, the light spilling out the windows onto the grass. It was very quiet out there, but you could hear the hum of electricity pouring through the thick wires overhead. For a moment or two I wondered if I should go back to the farmhouse. I had a feeling that if I didn't, the damage between us would harden like cement. But I also knew not to. I knew I was safer driving drugged and jumpy all the way back to the city, in the dark, on a motorcycle, than I would have been if I'd stayed in that house, that night, with my old friend.

Peculiar as it sounds, I can't recall how I heard what I heard next. Was there a phone call? I simply don't know. But this is what I read in the newspaper a few days later. Shortly after my departure, Justin fired a short blast from a machine gun into Duane's mouth. Brain tissue splattered against the library books. Several hours later (that's *hours*), local police were called. On arriving, they observed that the body had been "interfered with." Which meant moved from the living room to the kitchen to the porch. The study was in disarray: smashed furniture, lamps over-turned, a valuable Spanish acoustic guitar snapped off at the neck. One detail in particular snagged their attention: given where Justin claimed he was standing when the gun was discharged (self-defence, carving knife on the Persian carpet), the brain tissue appeared to be on the *wrong* part of the wall.

A blond woman with the eyes of a drowsy garter snake was also in the house. Justin's mother. It turned out she lived just down the road. A lawyer was also present.

By midnight the following day, Justin was a patient at the Bosley Centre for Criminal Psychiatry in Toronto, which, in a touch almost too literary to mention, faced the *kitchen* of my apartment several blocks away. In fact, I believe that first night, the day after the killing, I saw him standing at the window of his "room." With his hands in his pockets. I don't think he knew I lived nearby.

I never talked to the police. I've always had the suspicion that it was Justin's mother's idea to keep them from me, that she thought, as only the evil think, that I might do to her and her son what she, without question, would have done to me if our positions had been reversed. And more than once I woke up in the middle of the night with my heart thwacking at the notion that she might some-how—any way she *could*—implicate me in the murder. I say "murder" because I know that's what it was. I knew it then, I know it now. And they both know I know.

In the days that followed, the Bosley Centre looming across the streetcar tracks, I read more about the case, how Duane, at the time of his death, had been out on bail for the kidnapping and torture of a prostitute as well as the attempted murder of his *own* mother with a ball-peen hammer. Which accounted, I'm sure, for the hair rising on the back of my neck when I met him. Our instincts aren't there for nothing; they keep us alive. In a word, Justin Strawbridge had gone to town and brought the devil back. I have often wondered if he did it on purpose, if he set out that day to destroy his life.

The police, so said the newspaper, discovered a cache of weapons inside the farmhouse: two .38 revolvers, a metal-link whip, a second machine gun, nunchuks, a Tai-wanese Death Star, and "a weapon of decapitation." How banal, a rich boy doing designer drugs and collecting weapons, all paid for on his mother's dime.

"Just what a boy needs for a life in the country," said M., my first ex-wife. "How'd he like *War and Peace*, by the way?"

"We didn't get around to it."

"He'll have time now, I imagine." (She'd had a fling with him in university.)

I saw Justin only one more time after that glimpse in the window of the nuthouse. It was at his murder trial a year later. I ran into him in the courthouse bathroom at lunch; he was puffy and hungover, with a short haircut and an expensive grey suit. He'd put on weight and still carried around that metallic smell. Standing beside me at the urinal, he looked around briefly to make sure we were alone and then whispered, "Duane Hickok paid the ultimate price for busting my guitar." And then he winked!

I didn't go back to the courthouse after that. It sparked off too many ugly, confusing emotions. Part of me, *most* of me really, wanted to see him convicted. I couldn't get that revolting image of him doing somersaults in the dandelion field out of my head. And I was dismayed that this young man whom I had adored as no other young man in my early life, whom I had envied, even sought on occasion to imitate, this Justin had turned out to be a useless, parasitic bullshitter (Walt Whitman, my ass), a pretend musician, a pretend poet tied now forever to his mother in the sickest of knots ("I know what you did!") and therefore never, ever free to be anything but her failed son.

His mother, I'm told, paid a hundred and fifty grand for a chic WASP lawyer, a bloated gentleman in a brown suit who looked like an overfed bass. Mrs. Strawbridge didn't want "some fancy Jew showing off on the court-room steps." Certainly her son was in need of deft counsel. How about those brains on the wrong part of the wall? And how do you explain moving the body all over the downstairs? They did everything but pop a cigar in his mouth and dance with him.

After five days of deliberation, the jury found Justin guilty of manslaughter, but not of murder, which was the original indictment. They must have known, these twelve regular Canadians, that something was fishy, but they didn't have quite the goods for a murder conviction. And yes, I *was* disappointed, terrible as it is to say. I wanted something bad to happen to him. He ended up serving eighteen months in a minimum-security prison and then moved up north to a small Ontario city, where his mother still lives.

I was explaining all this to my wife as we looked across the dandelion field at the house with the crooked spine. It used to look like the house in Hitchcock's *Psycho*, but it didn't anymore. A crow cawed from a farmer's fence. In the far distance, a tractor moved across the gold-green canola fields. It was a tranquil scene. A flash of sunlight glinted off the windshield of a passing car. There was no horror here, no shadow of death; even the image of my naked friend somersaulting in the dandelions had lost its electric charge. I had expected more, a chill, *something*, but it was plainly gone.

Three children issued from the house, burbling down the porch stairs. One of them, a pencil-thin girl with blond hair and pink shorts, shrieked—the wind carried it across the grass to us—and tore off into the field, her brothers in pursuit. And when she'd gone fifty yards, running for the sake of running, she leapt into the air and wriggled like a fish rising from the water and then, from the sheer excitement of being outside and being alive, shrieked again. And in so doing she reminded me of my own daughter, all grown up now but once a child like that, so volatile and operatic. It was, I remembered, *her* I'd thought about that day in the dandelion field, my chest seizing with that terrible drug, a dread that I might miss out on her life. But I hadn't. I was lucky. That was the word for it. Lucky. Sometimes it's all these things come down to. Justin Strawbridge had a mother like his; I had a mother like mine.

And recalling Justin, jowly and hungover in the courtroom, his foolish haircut, his mouth full of lies, his forehead furrowed when he addressed the judge, I recalled—and told my wife about—another Justin Strawbridge.

I was fourteen, and Justin's family and my family went to a fancy resort up north for the Christmas holidays. Skiing, snowballs, sleigh rides and dress-up dinners. There was an American girl there, a year older than us: skinny, with a bony face, a clutch of thick blond hair and an over-bite. From Arkansas, I think. She spoke in a lazy, nasal accent, as if she was half amused all the time by everything. Sexiness creates mystery, yet she was so at ease with us— and consequently we with her—that she could have been one of the guys. Except she wasn't. Who could forget her name? Hailey Beauregard.

She must have been there with her parents, but I don't remember them. For a week we traipsed around the inn together, Justin and I both in love with her. She took us back to her room one evening and tried on a blue dress for us ("Y'all turn your backs now!") that she was planning to wear on the last night of the holidays, her bony arms popping from the sleeveless material. She was perspiring, I remember, and I could smell her and I found myself trying to sit near her, to stay within its range.

On the final Saturday night, there was a farewell party in the main ballroom. A local orchestra tootled Benny Goodman tunes. My parents danced; so did Justin's. A clear moon hung outside, cold air clarifying the trees and the lake.

But then, as a concession to "youth," the orchestra swung into a clunky version of Chubby Checker's hit song "The Twist," which had come out a few years earlier, and created a delirious new dancing style; people drying their bottoms with imaginary towels was how it looked, but at the time it figured as a powerful summons to get your hands under the shirt of a sweating teenage girl. Through a piece of singular luck, it was my turn to dance with Hailey when the song's opening saxophone bars honked from the stage. Swept up with excitement, grinding and twirling, I fancied I was cutting quite the figure, the very image of avant-garde youth, modernity and God knows what else. The crowd pulled back. Such attention, such appreciation on the lips of strangers! On it went; and on still further. I was *transported* by happiness.

The song ended, the final chords died away; the orchestra smiled smiles of good sportsmanship, the audience applauding—everyone, that is, except for a small, dark-eyed woman at the back of the hall. I gave a short bow, my heart thumping in my throat, my shirt soaked, and looked from face to face for *more*. But gradually, little by little, like a ship taking on water and slowly sinking, I noticed that no one seemed to be looking at *me*.

At that second, at that *very* second, as if my thoughts had been read, I felt a hand on my shoulder. It was Justin Strawbridge, and the slight pressure of his fingers, the almost maternal look on his face, told me everything I needed to know: that the roomful of white faces were beaming at the figure *beside* me, at the skinny girl in the sleeveless blue dress. It was her they were applauding.

I glanced over at Justin. A lesser boy would have melted into the crowd, would have washed his hands of me. (It seemed as if everyone else in the room had also perceived my misunderstanding at exactly the same moment.) But he was unwilling to let me swing alone in my public embarrassment.

It takes great courage to do something like that, especially when you're young.

Even after he and I fell out, when the damage from that incident in the dandelion field was so profound it couldn't be fixed, when we were truly ruined for each other, I always guarded that moment on the dance floor, kept it to the side of all the sordidness that followed. The innate "bigness" of his soul, before his foul appetites polluted it, rose unbidden to the surface. He was all the things that I had imagined that day I first laid eyes on him, in the doorway of a classroom, a creature whose perfection seemed so casual, so inevitable, that I felt a flutter of panic at the notion that I might be excluded from its glow.

5

My Life with Tolstoy

I t was an ill-advised journey. You don't go to Jamaica in August unless you grew up there. Too hot. And those roosters.

I wanted to go back because six months earlier I'd had such a swell time; got a great tan, danced on the beach, lost twenty pounds (all that Dexedrine) and had an affair with a skinny friend of my ex-wife. But when I came home, everything had slid sickeningly back into place. So I hocked a family heirloom and bought a discount plane ticket. Three weeks, no changes. M., my ex-wife, cooked me dinner the night before I left. Our seven-year-old daughter skittered into the kitchen in a pink track suit. She drew me a picture of a snake in a top hat. For good luck, she said. She knew I was frightened of flying.

"Don't say anything," M. said (she had something in her hand), "just give it a chance." She plopped a fat, gleaming paperback novel on the table in front of me. *War and*

Peace was a book I had avoided all my life, a book that, like Proust, only a stiff prison sentence could accommodate. But I loved M. and I knew she loved me, so I put the book in my shoulder bag the next morning (Jesus, what have you got in there, a brick?) and went to the airport.

It was 1988. I was thirty-eight years old.

I don't care for airports in the early morning. There's an alarming quality to people's faces at that hour, a pink brutishness, which extinguishes one's appetite for conversation. Stuck near the end of a long lineup to check in, I pulled *War and Peace* from my bag and scrutinized its cover. A Russian soldier reared up on the back of a horse, troops and cannon smoke and bayonets in the background.

"That's a marvellous book," a small voice said. An elderly woman behind me pointed a finger at my book. You could see she was not a person to intrude on a stranger, but that somehow the occasion, almost as if I were holding a photograph of someone she knew, justified it.

"I've read it three times," she said. "I'm getting ready for my fourth."

"You've read this three times?"

"I try to read it every five years."

I woke up with a hangover the next morning in a small Jamaican hotel. Finding myself in the same sun-baked room I had so happily occupied only six months before (except not alone), with the same soupy heat trying to squeeze in the door like a fat man, a dog barking mindlessly in the yard below, I couldn't recall for the life of me why it had seemed almost religiously important to get back here. I lay on my side like a wounded animal, waiting to be rescued by sleep's second act. When that failed, I opened *War and Peace* (this should do it) and, facing the white stucco wall, sweat already dribbling across my chest, began to read. We are at a gathering in the luxurious Petersburg apartments of Anna Pavlovna, gossip and confidante to the powers-that-be in the Russian court. It is 1805, the talk is of war and Napoleon. "Well, my prince, Genoa and Lucca are now no more than private estates of the Bonaparte family. . . ."

I have kept that copy of *War and Peace*, a spine-broken fifteen hundred pages held together by an elastic band. I cannot bear to throw it out (although I know my children will, twenty minutes after my passing). I have a check mark beside the paragraph where, even in the roller-coaster grip of a white rum hangover, I began to pay acute attention. I had been expecting, as one often finds with nineteenth-century novels, a kind of beautiful boredom. Instead, after only a few pages, I experienced one of those moments when you've been half listening to someone you don't take seriously and suddenly they say something so sharp, so true that it jars you physically, like the sound of expensive material ripping, and you realize *tout d'un coup* that you have completely underestimated them. Three days later I found myself stopping a stranger on the road outside my hotel and asking him, "Have you *read* this fucking thing?"

I was the only guest in the hotel. The staff had retreated to their homes in nearby towns. There was only the owner, a big-chested former policeman, and a beanpole bartender who subbed as cook. And me, of course, drifting up and down the hotel steps with *War and Peace* in my hand. Eating a solitary breakfast in the dining room. Wandering down the road to the beach where bare-breasted Italian girls played volleyball on the sand and I, like that poor prick in *Death in Venice*, read in the shade and waited for lunch.

It sounds bad, but it wasn't; because I had *War and Peace* and it pulled me out of my unhappiness as if I were on a rail. While the girls splashed in the waves (*"Tonio! Vieni amore! Vieni!"*), I followed the doings of a handful of Russian aristocrats on the eve of the Battle of Shöngrabern. The clumsy, illegitimate Pierre Bezuhov comes into a huge inheritance that transforms him overnight into Petersburg's most attractive bachelor. A teenage Natasha Rostova (after whom men have been naming their daughters for nearly a hundred and fifty years) thrills at the spectacle of her father's agile dancing at a court ball.

> "Look at papa," Natasha shouted to all the room (entirely forgetting that she was dancing with a grown-up partner), and ducking down till her curly

head almost touched her knees, she went off into her ringing laugh that filled the hall.

Then come the great battles. Sweet-natured Count Nicholas Rostov (Natasha's softie brother) finds himself in combat for the first time. Who, before Tolstoy, wrote a paragraph like this?

He gazed at the approaching French, and although only a few seconds before he had been longing to get at these Frenchmen and cut them down, their being so near seemed to him now so awful that he could not believe his eyes. "Who are they? What are they running for? Can it be to me? Can they be running to me? And what for? To kill me? Me, whom everyone is so fond of." He recalled his mother's love, the love of his family, and the enemy's intention of killing him seemed impossible . . . He snatched up his pistol and instead of firing it, flung it at the Frenchman and ran into the bushes with all his might.

Years later, I cemented an intuitive dislike for a television producer who turned her lovely, careerist features toward me one afternoon and claimed that the battle scenes in *War and Peace* had "bored" her (her ascendancy through the hierarchy of international television remains, depressingly, unchecked), whereas when I put the unforgiving *W&P* question to her husband, a spiky-haired local personality who had always struck me as an articulate flake, he raised his shoulders in a matter-of-fact gesture and said, "Oh, it's the greatest novel ever." I've adored him ever since.

Like the acting of Christopher Walken or the movies of Éric Rohmer, Tolstoy's magnum opus is a magnet for foolish opinions. It always has been. When it came out in 1869, a number of Moscow critics denounced it, some for containing too much French, others for being the self-regarding work of an aristocrat. One rancorous fellow attacked it for not "being either a novel or a novella." Most surprising, though, was Turgenev, who described the first twenty-eight chapters like this: "The thing is positively bad, boring and a failure . . . All those little details so cleverly noted, those psychological remarks which the author digs out of his heroes' armpits in the name of verisimilitude, all that is paltry and trivial." *Heroes' armpits?* Wow. Talk about missing the boat. Never mind. Joseph Stalin liked *W&P* so much that during the Nazi invasion he retooled the country's military outfits—gilded epaulettes, scarlet and white jackets, trousers with piping—so they might more closely resemble those in the novel.

On a less historical scale perhaps, M. and I went shopping for a high school for our by-then teenage daughter (no longer in pink sweatsuits). We interviewed one gentleman, the head of a reputable English department, who, after a gentle prod, announced that he didn't care for Tolstoy. "None of it," he said, crossing his legs and folding his arms defiantly. We chose another school. Once, when I was interviewing the "novelist" Ken Follett, he confided that *Anna Karenina* was "okay" but that he "didn't care at all" for *War and Peace*. All this delivered with a straight face from the man who brought us *The Hammer of Eden*.

But back to Jamaica. Late afternoons, I trudged home from the beach, two miles, and napped in my little white hot box. In the yard, the dogs slept in the shade. When I woke up, the sun had set but the room sweltered. I staggered onto the patio with my book and turned on the light and settled into a deck chair. A round moon rose up in the sky as a world-weary Prince Andrei Bolkonsky (the scene gives me goosebumps just recalling it) opens the shutters on a beautiful starry night and overhears the enchanting voice of a young girl, Natasha, on the floor above.

"Just look how lovely it is! Oh, how glorious! Do wake up, Sonya," and there were almost tears in her voice. "There was never, never such an exquisite night."

It just went on and on, a reading experience of such transport, of such tenderness (Tolstoy's compassion for his characters has the vividness of a mother suffering for her own child), that, for hours at a time, it blocked out the bleakness, the carnival's-left-town feel of a Caribbean resort in the off-season. Tolstoy is one of literature's great payoff artists. If you think about a novel (and let's not get too highfalutin about this) as a series of musical chords, say, C, Am, F, for example, then Tolstoy, more than any other writer I've experienced, understood what chord the reader needs, *really* needs to hear next: the inevitable G, the progression's perfect consummation. Which is why Tolstoy can make a reader so deliriously happy. (Unlike Chekhov, who, like Charlie Parker, follows a series of unpredictable chord changes that make his short stories seem both atonal and at the same time completely lifelike.)

Writing *War and Peace* was a happy time for Tolstoy. You can feel it in the prose, in the ineffable *lift* of some of the book's 125 scenes. He was already a bit of a literary star when he started it in 1862. *Youth* and *The Cossacks*, both novellas, had already come out in literary journals and made quite the splash. People wondered, Who is this guy? And unlike his contemporary Dostoevsky, Count Lev Nikolayevich Tolstoy (pronounced by Russian speakers with the emphasis on the second vowel) didn't have any money worries; he was an independently wealthy aristocrat who lived on an inherited four-thousand-acre estate with a woman who, at that point anyway, adored him and believed ardently in his gifts. Writing in her diary, Sofia confided, "Not one person in a million, I dare say, is as happy as we are . . . Nothing affects me as strongly as his ideas and his talent." Sofia also, and this seems almost unimaginable today, copied out most of the 1,500-page *W&P* manuscript at least *seven times*. "Have I changed," she wrote, "or is the book really very good?" Tolstoy was never so joyful again and, for my money, never wrote so well again.

One morning I zoomed into the hotel restaurant and spotted an inordinately good-looking young man sitting at a table, having coffee. I had just finished the section where Rostov takes a nighttime sleigh ride with the young Sonya, the moon hanging in the sky, bells on the horses jingling. It was a scene which had so exhilarated me, so excited my faith in romantic love, the notion that all things were still possible, even for me, that I had been unable to sit still and had finally shot out of the room. And now, look, a human being! Tanned, with a Roman nose, perfect teeth, he looked like a movie star. When he opened his mouth to return my greeting, I heard a soft Australian accent. I plied him with questions. He was a musician, taking a holiday. That's nice. And is your band doing well? Quite well. Do you play at dances and stuff? No, we play stadiums. Stadiums? "I'm with Midnight Oil," he said, and rather shyly, too.

He stayed for three days; we had breakfast together each morning, on one of which I read him the passage about Natasha and the starry night. I never saw him again after that, but I've always remembered his fresh good looks, his patient interest in Tolstoy. Years and years later I interviewed the lead singer for Midnight Oil—I forget his name, the bald guy—and I asked him about the young man in Jamaica, the bass guitarist, and I heard he'd quit the band after only a year or two, hadn't liked the life and had gone off and opened up a surf shop somewhere on the Queensland coast, which made me like him even more.

One afternoon, as I flopped soft-tummied and sweating in a beach chair not fifty feet from the Italians *("Ciao! Mia, ciao!")*, a pair of big-toothed California girls (they stayed at an all-inclusive, miles down the beach) struck up a conversation with me. Seeing that I was reading Tolstoy, one of them said, "What do you do?"

"I'm a model," I said. And they stayed; they stayed the whole afternoon, and when they left they invited me to meet them later that evening. What excitement. Company! Conversation! (I had taken to eating my lunch in front of the mirror.) But when I turned up later that night, fluffy-haired and chirpy, at a cliff-side restaurant, I saw them stealing their way across the patio. (It irritates me to this day.) The one in the lead caught sight of me; her fingers reached guiltily for an earlobe, an involuntary gesture Tolstoy would have enjoyed, and told me, get this, that they had already eaten. *Already eaten?* Embarrassed, shocked, speechless and then enraged, I said, "I'm going over there for a drink," and hurried to the empty bar. I drank several ice-cold Red Stripes so fast they made my eyes burn. I felt like I was putting out a fire.

I walked home that night under a beautiful moon. On the main floor of the hotel, behind a metal grille and curtains, I could make out the blue glare of a television set. The owner, that big ex-cop, was watching *Scarface* with Al Pacino. I coughed into my hand, then again with the vague hope that he might call me in for a visit—his wife was teaching school in Kingston—but no luck. I heard a murmur of confidential laughter. The girl who did the housecleaning was in there.

Later that night, Tolstoy just about finished me off. (Never get too comfortable with a Russian writer.) Natasha—my Natasha—is being seduced by a worthless playboy at the opera.

> When she was not looking at him, she felt that he was looking at her shoulders, and she could not help trying to catch his eyes that he might rather look in her face. But as she looked into his eyes, she felt with horror that, between him and her, there was not that barrier of modest reserve she had always been conscious of between herself and other men. In five minutes she felt—she did not see how—that she had come fearfully close to this man.

News gets back to her fiancé, Prince Andrei, and the marriage is off.

I turned off the bedside lamp. A double disaster in paradise.

Jump ahead now to 2004, almost twenty years after that night in Jamaica. I sat on the porch with my nineteen-year-old son on a fall evening in Kensington Market in Toronto. His young face wore a look of controlled horror and I dared barely glance at him. A summertime romance, white-hot, had come to an unexpected end a few weeks before. First the dreadful premonitions, then panicky long-distance calls (she went to university in another city), one of which found the young lady in a bar. To his question, "Are you breaking up with me?" (how courageous, the nakedness of it!), she replied offhandedly, "Yes."

So there we were, he and I, sitting side by side, staring at the damp street. "You know that thing I was afraid of happening?" he said.

I was almost unable to catch my breath. "Yes."

"Well, it happened," he said. Someone had informed him by phone. His girlfriend had gone to bed with an old lover. He couldn't stop smoking cigarettes and he couldn't stop imagining the things you should never imagine but always do. You could see it playing out on his pale, childlike features: *She does this to him, he does that to her.* We've all done it, but you'd step in front of a car to spare your own son doing it.

"I think she's making a terrible mistake," I said, use-lessly. In the long silence (puff, puff), I found myself think-ing about Natasha and her betrayal of Prince Andrei.

"I'll never take her back," my son said.

Then, miraculously (but not surprisingly), a few months later, just after Christmas, his girlfriend suffered a change of heart. It started with an emissary ("She really misses you"), then a "surprise" encounter at a party ("If you keep looking at me like that, I'm going to have to kiss you"). Where did she learn to *speak* like that? Had she read *War and Peace* too?

So there we were again, bundled in coats on the porch. Snowflakes, some large, some small, settled indecisively on the front lawn. I knew what he was thinking. Recrimi-nations and brutal quizzes lay just ahead for both of them. "What if she does it again?" he said.

"You know what Tolstoy says."

"What?"

I said, "Tolstoy says a woman can never hurt you the same way twice."

"You think that's true, Dad?"

"Yes," I said finally, "I believe it is."

With a swift but circumspect movement, Natasha came nearer; still kneeling, and carefully taking his hand, she bent her face over it and began kissing it, softly touching it with her lips.

"Forgive me," she said in a whisper, lifting her head and glancing at him. "Forgive me."

"I love you," said Prince Andrei.

Writers sleep better if they trick themselves into believing that the great masterpieces of literature were written in old-age homes—by the grey and the venerable, in other words. Kazuo Ishiguro *(Remains of the Day)* confessed to a reporter that he'd ruined an afternoon for himself (possibly his life, he joked) when, on one imprudent occasion, he did some elementary math and discovered how old his favourite writers had been when they produced their *chefs-d'oeuvre*. I did the same thing myself a while ago and I now share his dismay: Virginia Woolf, only forty-two when she wrote *Mrs. Dalloway*; Scott Fitzgerald, an unforgivable twenty-nine with *The Great Gatsby*. Joyce's *Ulysses* (punishingly dull but nevertheless—), thirty-nine. Lev Nikolayevich Tolstoy was forty-one when he finished *War and Peace*, arguably the greatest novel ever written, after which, instead of taking a Caribbean vacation, he launched into an obsessive study of ancient Greek and then took up the bicycle. (Russ Meyer, by the way, was the same age when he finished *Faster, Pussycat! Kill! Kill!*)

When *I* finished *War and Peace*, I had a hell of a tan and I wanted (a lifetime bad habit) to keep the party going. I came back to Toronto and one of the first things I did was to buy a no-nonsense hardback of *Anna Karenina*. But it didn't work this time. Something was different; I couldn't engage; the novel didn't block out the dozen worries that nibbled at my attention. I thought it was the book. It was as if—and I'm not convinced this isn't the truth—Tolstoy had used all his favourite characters in *W&P* and was now working through the B-list. After a hundred or so pages, I put the book aside. And that's where it stayed for seven years, until 1992.

I was greyer, fatter, and witnessing, with escalating upset, the death of a love affair. Another love affair. (Love, I've learned, is a living creature and when it's dying, like an animal too weak to care who feeds it, the signs are unmistakable.) Molly Wentworth and I spoke to each other with excessive caution, the way people speak who have lost their natural ease with each other, a mother tongue that somehow the two of you have forgotten.

There are ways, of course, to put lipstick on the corpse, to get it up and dancing, however grotesquely. Get married, buy a house, have a baby, that's what some couples do. But there's a fourth, less binding option: take a holiday together. And that's what we did. At five-thirty on a black, snowy morning in Toronto, a limousine picked up me and Molly and my old hardback of *Anna Karenina* and drove us to oblivion.

By the time we got to the hotel in Bangkok, it was as if I had taken two hits of old-fashioned blotter acid. The world shimmered—all those hours on the plane. (She had slept like a child, her long, beautiful eyelashes twitching. What was she dreaming about? Beside her, like the troll under the bridge, I glared at six consecutive films, one after the other.)

It was a lovely hotel, the river winding below our window. At night you could see long boats moving on the water. But nothing could save us, not sex or gin or Santa Claus.

"Is anything wrong?"

"No. You?"

"No, I'm fine."

Ugh.

(*Anna Karenina*, in four lines.)

I stayed in the hotel room, the city a smoggy, uninteresting blur outside, and started *Anna K.* for the second time. Molly walked through the city, visited the university, I'm not sure what else. There's a way you read when you travel; it is, in itself, a kind of transport, the purity with which you pay attention. You never read like that at home. In fact, as the years have gone by and with them a dozen other trips, it has occurred to me that reading, all on its own, may well be the best reason *to* travel. This time out, I was so entranced with *Anna Karenina*, the story of an unfaithful woman getting fed, however beautifully, into Tolstoy's lawn mower, that the events in the book became more real to me, more important to me, than Bangkok's foul air, my girlfriend's unreachable unhappiness, or the bar upstairs where one evening I encountered an old friend from university, a professional traveller who, like many professional travellers, had no curiosity about anything he encountered and talked about himself with an almost autistic insistence.

I hurried back to my room downstairs—back to Tolstoy, back to Levin's unhappy thwarting at the hands of young Dolly. Tolstoy had such excitement about romantic love (at least for a while). You can feel him purr during his great love scenes. He adored the red-light, green-light nature of it, its democratic stranglehold. You're never too rich, too beautiful, too stupid, too broke, too *anything* to resist its crooking finger. Unlike Chekhov, whose unhappy characters tend to stay unhappy, Tolstoy believed (once again, for a while) that romantic, sexualized love had the power to transform people, to make them happy. It lured Prince Andrei from a pit of malignant self-absorption; made Pierre Bezuhov into an adult; thrilled Anna Karenina for the only time in her life. Eventually it ripened and completed Levin as a man.

One morning Molly and I were having breakfast in the upstairs bar. I was spooning honeyed yogurt into my mouth with a greedy urgency.

"I don't mean to be insulting," Molly said with a strained smile, "but you're making quite a racket over there."

That, for those who don't recognize it, is the sound of a woman who no longer wants you. It reminded me—

with the suddenness of someone smashing a hammer on the table—of a scene that I had read only days before, where Anna views her husband's ears (they stick out) with revulsion.

A few days later, the sun was setting over the river. Such a melancholy time, the boats with little bow lanterns, like fireflies, drifting downstream with the current. I was caught midway in that famous scene where Anna, having fled her family, sneaks back to her former house to visit her nine-year-old son. Her husband is asleep downstairs. She bribes a servant, she starts up the stairs—I knew that this was a one-time moment in literature, that I would never again get to experience the unfolding of this scene *without knowing its outcome*. Would she get to see the little boy or not? It felt as urgent as a crisis in my own life and I feared, I actually feared, that Molly with her blond hair and sharp features, those beautiful eyelashes, would wander into the room at the very second and spoil everything. I leapt up from the bed and locked the door to the room.

The end of a love affair comes in different ways. For Molly, it was the spectacle of me wolfing down a dish of yogurt (as if someone might steal it); for me, it was the moment I decided to shut her out of the room and all the things inside it.

Pretty much everything Tolstoy wrote after *Anna K.* is so top-heavy with pedantry or moral instruction that you can't finish it. The danger signs were there even in the divine *War and Peace*: that dull section where Pierre joins the Freemasons; or the novel's last, dreadful chapter. (Surely the real ending comes forty pages earlier, with Prince Andrei's son eavesdropping on a favourite uncle downstairs.) There's trouble brewing here and there in *Anna Karenina* too, in Levin's tiresome reflections on rural agriculture. How I long to stop strangers when I see these books under their arms, to implore them to skip those sections so they won't leave such magnificent works on a note of anticlimax.

From 1881 onwards, Tolstoy underwent a spiritual crisis that was characterized by great, some would say insane, extremes, a disgust with sex, a disdain for literature, an abandonment of secular pleasures, even riding his bicycle. ("Daddy loves giving things up," one of his daughters wrote snidely in her diary.) This unforgiving embrace of Christianity (with a few suggestions for its improvement, naturally) made him a kind of holy figure in Russia and attracted devotees and lunatics from all over the country, many of whom stayed at the house, much to the fury of Madame Tolstoy. But even when he was out in the barn dressed like a peasant, making his own boots and calling his wife a whore, there remained a few dazzling literary turns in the, by now, old coot. It was as if every so often Tolstoy couldn't stop being Tolstoy, couldn't stand in the way of his own nagging genius.

People know *The Death of Ivan Ilyich* (1886), but for some reason almost no one I've talked to has read the extraordinary novella *Master and Man*, which he wrote when he was seventy-two years old. I came across it by accident years after I thought I knew all the Tolstoy hits, when, out of a nostalgia for a more excitable time in my life (literature leaves fainter traces as the years go by), I sat in on an undergraduate course in the nineteenth-century Russian novel at the University of Toronto. (I had time as well as nostalgia on my hands.) *Master and Man*, I discovered, is the great Tolstoy buried treasure. It's a very simple story indeed. A peasant, Nikita, and his master, a lumber merchant, set off on a winter afternoon to conclude a deal in a neighbouring village. A storm comes up; they lose their way; night falls. As the two drift through a zone of lunar frigidity ("It sometimes seemed that the sledge was standing still and the countryside was rolling away behind them"), what the reader experiences may well be the best description of winter in literature.

Tolstoy's wife, Sofia, who looked after the business end of things, was away when Tolstoy finished *Master and Man*. In her absence he sold it to a magazine for next to nothing. Big trouble when she came back. Raging through the house (the servants cringing behind the furniture), she accused him of sleeping with the editor and raised such a row that Tolstoy declared the marriage over and went to his room to pack. Not to be outdone, Sofia ran outside into the Russian winter clad in only a nightdress and a dressing gown. Wearing underwear and a vest, with no shirt, Tolstoy chased after her. Once rescued, the distraught wife took to her bed. Unable to endure her unhappiness, Tolstoy relented and cancelled the magazine deal. But two days after the rights were formally returned, their seven-year-old son, Vanichka, a gifted, sweet-natured boy, developed scarlet fever and died. His parents, the quarrel over the manuscript forgotten, sat together on the sofa, "almost unconscious with grief."

A word to the wise, if I may, about *Master and Man* in particular and about Tolstoy in general. Be careful. Tolstoy is not afraid to hurt you. When the timber merchant realizes that Nikita is freezing to death, he does something so astonishing—and then *not* astonishing—that you have the feeling of someone sticking a hand into your chest. I won't ruin the story for you but, in a word, this is not the guy to read before your afternoon nap.

Which brings us happily and finally to the present. Late fall in Havana, Cuba. Not the end but nearing the final chapters of my life with Tolstoy. I didn't bring him with me this time, but then again, he is somebody you never quite leave behind. Once infected, never cured. And, like Proust, Tolstoy changes not just the way you see the world but occasionally even the way you experience it. Sometimes, in fact, I feel I've come to lean on Tolstoy rather too much; have seen him in too many of my own life's events (Oh! Just like that moment in—); have quoted him too often (as I do with the Beatles when I try to inspire my son's sporadically deflated musical aspirations). I remember once, when I was working in television, a producer raised her head in indignation from a script I'd written about a Manitoba violinist and snapped, "No more Tolstoy, okay!"

So—a last Tolstoy moment before I go. It's a sunny day in Havana, the wind high and whipping through the power lines outside my hotel window; the ocean is bluer than yesterday but still wild and white-capped. Many years have lapsed since Bangkok. I have remarried, but I have left my wife at home this time, have come for a holiday in my own company, something I have not done for many years.

Yesterday I took a walk along the seawall. A wedding procession roared by; it looked like a scene from *Godfather Two*, when Michael Corleone goes to Cuba. Later I had a coffee on the terrace of the Hotel Inglaterra in the old city. (What does one do with all this time on one's hands? I can't quite remember.) Another wedding procession, beribboned cars from the fifties, a white bride and a black groom perched on the back of a convertible. A Frenchman at the next table tells me Havana is a big town for public weddings. Which makes me think about my own wedding only a few years ago. We had it in the living room of our new house (my "starter" home, age fifty-six) in Kensington Market. My second ex-wife, Catherine, stood with our son, both of them lanky and lovely. How lucky I am, I thought, looking at them, that they are still here, still part of my life.

And there's M., my first ex-wife—the one who gave me Tolstoy all those years ago—laying out the food and bossing the help around (she wants the food table against the wall, not "in the middle of the goddamn room"). Our daughter, all grown up now, tall and blond and somehow extravagant even at rest, calls the room to order. She is the Master of Ceremonies tonight and begins to read, stopping a sentence in. "I hope I can get through this without bursting into tears," she says. The room falls silent. She continues.

> Prince Andrei loved dancing . . . and chose Natasha for a partner because Pierre pointed her out to him, and because she was the first pretty girl who caught his eyes. But he had no sooner put his arm around that slender, supple waist, and felt her stirring so close to him, and smiling so close to him, than the intoxication of her beauty flew to his head.

Looking at my daughter and then at Rachel, my wife of only a few minutes now (so pretty in her black dress), I feel a wave of almost unendurable good fortune. And I think: You must not ask more from life than this.

6

Ladies and Gentlemen,
the Beatles!

T he other night I did a search on my eight-
year-old computer and discovered that there
were over 250 different documents where I
mentioned the Beatles by name. Book reviews, a screen-
play (unproduced), a novel, a magazine article on Tolstoy,
diaries, letters, even a wine review. They certainly got to
me, those boys.

And so when I started to write this book, on going back
to places where you've suffered, I had to mention them.
Because if you're my age and have ever suffered in the
name of love, chances are you've done it with the Beatles
in the background.

I went out and bought the paperback of Bob Spitz's
2005, brick-sized Beatle biography. It's a beautifully written, nine-hundred-page travail. Mr. Spitz spent six years
on it, moved to Liverpool for six months, split up with his

wife over it. But something surprising and vaguely dis-
comforting happened. I got through maybe a hundred
pages and then I stopped. I knew all the stories and I just
didn't care to hear them again. I was Beatled-out. A new
verb, that, to be Beatled-out: to love something like you'll
probably never love anything again, but to have had
enough for one lifetime.

But let's go back for a moment or two. It was 1987,
George Harrison had just released his final album, *Cloud
Nine*, and I was going to London to interview him. Shooting through the darkness at 37,000 feet above the Atlantic,
I stared into space with the *gravitas* of a man going to his
execution. I had two stiff drinks to calm down, but they
skated weightlessly over my excitement. The image of
John, Paul and George singing "This Boy" into a single
microphone on *The Ed Sullivan Show* in 1964 was para-
lyzing.

A list of do-not-do's: For God's sake, don't ask him if
he got a lot of girls. Or if he ever felt "weird" about kick-
ing Pete Best out of the band. Nor does he need to know
that you once had a skinny girlfriend in Kansas City who,
substituting a perfume bottle for a microphone, used to
sing "If I Fell" in front of her bedroom mirror. Oh, and
don't bother telling him about Raissa and that time you
heard "Don't Let Me Down" at five o'clock in the morning in a Paris café and nearly died of longing for her.

Don't tell him your publisher moonlights occasionally in a Beatles cover band. And don't ask the one question that no one on earth can answer except those four young men in the limo: *What was it like to be in the Beatles?*

In preparation for the interview, I spent a sunny morning driving around Liverpool with Nancy Rutledge, a middle-aged real estate agent. Nancy was George's girlfriend for a few months when they were both sixteen, but with that hard-headed common sense so typical of northerners she didn't appear to think it was a big deal.

She drove me to the Cavern Club, or its replacement rather. Unwise city fathers tore down the original in 1973 to make room for an underground rail loop. It was here, under the famous brick archway, that the boys made it big, playing 292 shows, afternoon and night, from 1961 to 1963, the last gig only a month or so after recording "She Loves You." It was also here that a gay young record store owner, Brian Epstein, fell in love at first sight (those black leather jackets helped) and offered to get them a record deal. Which, after an imprudent executive at Decca Records told him that guitar bands were "finished," he did.

While Nancy stopped at a pastry store to pick up a birthday cake for a client, I hopped out of the car and phoned a friend in Toronto, himself a scrupulous Beatles fan.

"Guess where I am?" I said breathlessly.

"Where?"

"I'm at the Cavern Club." But his response was not what I'd hoped for.

"They tore down the Cavern Club years ago," he said.

"Yes, I know that, but . . ." I began to explain but the moment was lost, and walking away from the red phone booth (Nancy waiting for me in a restaurant) I was perplexed by my friend's coldness, his appetite to diminish my excitement, and I was again reminded that you have to be careful to whose ears you bring good news, that the world, even your friends, sometimes *especially* your friends, doesn't always wish you good fortune. Still, it troubled me, and for the next few days I found myself returning to it.

We looked at other spots: George's childhood home, the hairdressing salon where Ringo's wife, Maureen, worked, the Strawberry Field orphanage and the Casbah Coffee Club, which was run by Pete Best's mom. "Pete's fine now," Nancy said brightly. "He had a rough spell, you can only imagine, but he's gotten quite famous, even a bit rich."

She had a two o'clock showing, a triplex in a nearby town, and asked would I mind if she got on the road. Which was a nice way of saying that she didn't have much more to say about George or any particular nostalgia about that time of her life. Dropping me off in front of my hotel, she unwound the window and said, "Ask him if he remembers my little blue car." And then, glancing over her shoulder, she pulled into the light Liverpool traffic without, I bet, giving me or the Beatles another thought.

Two days later, I followed a polite, normal-looking young woman up a flight of stairs to the third floor of George Harrison's pleasantly appointed office, Handmade Films, in London. The camera crew had already arrived and was setting up. From what I gathered, they'd just returned from shooting an interview with Mikhail Gorbachev in Moscow. The Soviet Union was disintegrating, but this, meeting George Harrison, was apparently a bigger deal. Like the pharmaceutical supplier who had sat next to me in the plane on the way over, they knew more about the Beatles than an adult should know, than *anyone* should know: which verse of "Help" was forgotten during the Miami leg of *The Ed Sullivan Show*, that George got a black eye when a drunken Pete Best fan head-butted him outside the washroom in the Cavern Club. That Paul McCartney's father, after hearing the just-written "She Loves You" (acoustic guitars in the living room), suggested a minor lyric change: "Yes, yes, yes would be better," he offered.

Two cameramen, two soundmen, a producer, two assistant producers and a lighting "guy." They were nervous or excited, I couldn't tell which, but they wouldn't shut up. I wasn't doing any better. Like a man about to be shot, I stood by the window looking out at the empty trees, the thin sunlight, a woman walking a dog. February in London, everything so sad, so defeated. It was, of course, anxiety cloaking itself as melancholy. Some people get hungry when they're frightened; I get sad, which I knew, but it didn't help. Not a bit.

I heard a voice behind me, the up-and-down musicality of a Liverpool accent. "I didn't realize it was television. Give me a sec to brush my hair." A slim man in a rumpled shirt and worn blue jeans stood in the doorway, smiling pleasantly. His face was older, more deeply lined than I'd expected. He extended his hand to the barrel-chested cameraman who was staring at him as if he'd just seen a cobra standing on its tail.

"I'm George Harrison," he said.

I was thirteen when I first heard "She Loves You" and found it, with its unusual chord progression, G to Bm (folk song chords), something of a disappointment. It *almost* went where you wanted it to—that great start!—but then didn't. And that anticlimactic guitar riff just before the second verse made me wonder what all the fuss was about.

But a few months later I heard "I Saw Her Standing There." No song, no piece of music before or since, has ever churned me like that. That busy bass line, a snare drum whack that seemed to hang just a split second behind the beat, and Paul's inimitable shriek (try it sometime) just before the guitar solo made me want to throw something, swear, scream out the window, as if my young body simply could not contain the sensations it was experiencing. And the count-in, for me the most galvanic count-in in rock music.

Unhappy with the song's original second line—it was a sugary McCartney flourish comparing the girl to a "beauty queen"—John Lennon smirked and suggested "You know what I mean" instead. I've always felt that that exchange was the key to the Beatles' collaboration, why it worked and why, on their own, they never quite matched their former, alchemical *je ne sais quoi*.

My father, whose interests extended to golf, Scotch and sleeping with my mother's friends, scolded me in the car one afternoon for wasting my allowance on Beatle magazines. It wasn't the scolding that stung, it was the waft of contempt that came with it. I examined these glossy publications with a kind of forensic scrutiny. I was looking for something, an explanation that might diffuse the tension in my body. Nearly forty years later I came across a passage in a Chekhov short story, and I understood not what I was looking for in those pictures of four young men in black suits and white shirts but what I was *experiencing* while I was looking at them. In the 1888 Chekhov story "The Beauties," a teenage boy catches sight of a peasant girl as she flits about inside a hut in the Russian countryside. Chekhov writes:

Whether it was envy of her beauty, or that I was regretting that the girl was not mine, and never would be, or that I was a stranger to her . . . or whether, perhaps, my sadness was that peculiar feeling which is excited by the contemplation of real beauty, God only knows.

Sadness, it has since occurred to me, is an inexplicable response to great art. I felt it when I flipped through those Beatle magazines the same way I would feel it later when I came across a description of a party in Scott Fitzgerald's *The Great Gatsby*:

There was music from my neighbour's house through the summer nights. In his blue gardens men and girls came and went like moths among the whisperings and the champagne and the stars.

It is, this sadness, a reaction to something that you can never possess, that always moves away from you no matter how fast or how hard you try to grab it.

Because of Ringo Starr, because of the way he *looked* behind a pearl grey set of Ludwig drums, because of the almost unendurable happiness that I imagined he was feeling, I chose to be a drummer. When my parents left the house for the evening, I hurried to my mother's bedroom on the second floor and put "It Won't Be Long" on her stereo. Tap, tap, tap went my little knife blades, dancing along the top of her glass dressing table. Sometimes my brother, Dean, stuck his head in the door; he wasn't yet so furious at life, but rather remote and admirable, and I adored his approval. He'd look in, watch for a moment and then, quietly closing the door, return to the baseball game on his maroon bedroom radio.

The snow melted outside my window; ice fell from the eavestroughs and the Beatles released "I Want to Hold Your Hand." Was there ever so irresistible a sight as the three of them stepping forward to the microphones to harmonize.

I played with real drumsticks now; on school books, on walls, on my thighs. I played after school, after dinner. I practised all the time. But I could never manage the drum roll that comes at the end of the song's titular line in "I Want to Hold your Hand." Was it a hand-over-hand thing or was it a succession of single, staccato beats on descending drums? Snare, tom-tom, floor tom. I must have listened to it two hundred times, picking up the needle, dropping it back down, picking it up, dropping it down, picking it up, dropping it down. ("Jesus H. Christ!" my mother shrieked down the stairs.)

But I couldn't figure it out. Ever. In fact only the other day I saw a black-and-white tape of Ringo doing it on *The*

Ed Sullivan Show. The camera went in for a close-up. I replayed it. Then replayed it again, until a kind of sickening sensation spread through my body.

I must have already been thwarted by other things in life—skating to the left, drawing a tree, juggling, tuning a guitar, slide rules, patching a bicycle tire—but this impasse was a pinching lesson on the exigencies of talent. Which is to say, in the parlance of my ex-wife, M., "Sometimes you're fucked just by who you are."

I wonder, though, if the unlucky drummer, Pete Best, could do it. If I ever met him, I'd have a million questions, but that would certainly be one. Can *you* do the drum roll in "I Want to Hold Your Hand"? I bet not. I bet if he could—

It was a shameful episode and I have, sadly, always associated it with the only time I saw the Beatles perform live. I was fourteen years old, and I was bewitched by a girl from, in my mother's dreadful parlance, "the wrong side of the tracks." Her name was Shauna. ("Only girls who have sex in automobiles are called Shauna," my mother said.) Short, with teased hair and a sleeveless, fuzzy sweater, Shauna turned up at a Sunday morning church group; all the pretty girls in Forest Hill went there; but no one knew Shauna. She just appeared out of nowhere, this creature in a cloud of erotic pollen.

"What's a girl like that even *doing* in this neighbourhood?" my mother asked. By which she meant that girls like Shauna invariably got themselves knocked up and then asked for a whole lot of money to go away. My mother, a curious mixture of authentic left-wing liberalism and cruel snobbery.

I ignored her admonitions, of course. And who wouldn't? I came home late at night that fall with leaves all over my sweater and my eyes so bright they could peel the paint off walls.

Summer came; boys took off their ties and wrote exams in a holy silence; and then we left the city for our white house in the country. Like a Chinese water torture, my mother's acidic disapproval chewed through my affection for Shauna until, in a moment of disgraceful compliance, I allowed her to dictate an ending-things letter which I left that same afternoon for the mailman in the box at the top of our lane. I did this in exchange for permission to go to Toronto to see the Beatles at Maple Leaf Gardens. Frozen with embarrassment and shame—a month had since lapsed—I sat next to Shauna in a crowd of twenty thousand hysterical teenagers. Even the man who unpacked Ringo's snare drum got a scream that day. Staring straight ahead, I could feel Shauna looking at me. I could feel her waiting. Then she said, "You could at least *look* at me." But there was a tone to her voice which I hadn't expected, a kind of breezy disdain that said, "Don't think you're so important, bub."

I know the Beatles played "Long Tall Sally" that day; I know Shauna asked me if she could borrow my binoculars, I know that when John Lennon clowned around on-stage—he was pretending to be Frankenstein—the crowd blew the ceiling off the Gardens. I remember all that only fuzzily. But those words, or rather the *way* she said them, retain a peculiar freshness, like an audible report card of someone who has caught you at your most unattractive.

Five years go by. I'm in Paris with Justin Strawbridge. It's my first time in Europe and I'm experiencing the unhappy fragility of waking up after dark in a foreign country with nothing having turned out the way you had hoped it would. It was five o'clock in the morning, I was in an over-lit café drinking a glass of red wine—how awful it tasted, like a glass of blood—when "Don't Let Me Down" came on the jukebox. By 1969, the Beatles didn't much like each other, but even in the initial descending chords of that song, the announcement as it were, it's as if all antagonisms have been momentarily forgotten and the four of them revert to a kind of mother tongue that not even the insistent and toxic presence of Yoko Ono could disrupt. "Don't Let Me Down" is one of the great Beatles buried treasures, as effortless in its execution as the gait of a loose-limbed country boy.

That early morning in Paris, it seemed to me that I'd never heard the song properly before, that it was, in fact, a miniature symphony with complete, individual movements. Except that I liked it more, it moved me more, than Beethoven or Mozart. It had that thing which all great Beatles songs have, which *all* great art has, a sense of inevitability, that the progression of chords could only go in that order, and only with those lyrics; that if only you'd been given the first few bars you could have written it yourself.

And it occurred to me also (Justin talking to a prostitute in the doorway) that I was going to lose Raissa Shestatsky to another man, that I was losing her even while I was standing here. And those lyrics: Lennon leaning obscenely close to the microphone to emphasize the dirtiness of the words. That business about getting done by his girlfriend. The notion that I might never see Raissa naked again hit me like a kick in the stomach.

Why, I wondered, had I come to France, to this grey, grey city, when my life was so obviously elsewhere: an apartment on Major Street where I had left a young girl sleeping fitfully? What had I been thinking!

And then came the song's final notes, that piano, wistful, fading, like a girl waving from a train.

I was in Casablanca in the seventies piddling about and waiting for my life to begin when I met a young Iranian,

Arghavan Gholami, one afternoon. We were in a café in the French quarter, everyone uneasily stoned on hashish, Raissa long gone, when he began to talk about growing up listening to the Beatles in a small city on the Caspian Sea.

The Caspian Sea?

It was like talking to a Beatles scholar with an Arab accent (as momentarily displacing as a Chinese woman talking with a Jamaican accent). Did I know, Arghavan asked, that Ringo had played drums on the album version of "Love Me Do" but that a studio musician had sat in for the 45? That George Harrison had played bass on "She Said, She Said" because Lennon and McCartney had had a violent row which concluded with Paul storming out of the studio? That the lyric about butterflies in "It's Only Love" seemed so corny to Lennon (even though he wrote it himself) that it wrecked the song for him? That Beatles producer George Martin lifted the cello strokes in "Eleanor Rigby" from the soundtrack to Hitchcock's *Psycho*? (Another surprise.)

"If you want to know how Ringo got the job," Arghavan said, "listen to the drumming on 'Anna.' It's like a set of drums falling down the stairs."

Until that day, I'd always assumed the Beatles were my possession, that other people liked them, sure, but I had a special rapport with them. But listening to this young Iranian, I began to suspect maybe that wasn't the case.

And the idea that it might *not* be gave me a confusing sense of comfort, that I was not, therefore, alone with this peculiar sensation of longing or sadness or incompleteness that I experienced whenever I heard their music or saw them in photographs.

All this ran through my head as I waited for the cameraman to stop fiddling and tinkering with the lighting, George Harrison already seated opposite me, patient, waiting to begin. For reasons too inane to elaborate on, I had decided to conduct the interview with no notes—I must have wanted Mr. Harrison to be impressed.

"We're ready over here," the producer said.

Harrison drummed on the arm of his chair and looked up pleasantly.

"So George," I began, my mind wiped clean as an afterschool blackboard, "what was it like being in the Beatles?"

The room sagged. The producer looked paralyzed with dismay. Even the cameramen, trained like pointers, flinched. Harrison paused. He looked away, thinking of an answer, determined to take the question seriously, and with it, the person who asked it.

"Well, you know, for a *first* job, it wasn't too bad."

Everyone relaxed. With a guy like that, you can't go wrong.

My memory of what he said after that is patchy. Luckily, I kept the raw footage, and looking at it today, I see a kind and thoughtful Harrison responding with playfulness, while off camera a voice (mine), a full octave higher than normal, asks overly complicated questions punctuated by explosions of pointless laughter (again mine). We talked about all sorts of things: his older sister whom he visited in Canada at the outset of Beatlemania, the late Brian Epstein, gardening, Eric Clapton, Monty Python, even the American playwright Tennessee Williams. Were his last plays bad or was it just the critics? Harrison wondered aloud, an elegant, pre-emptive defence of his new album and the hostility it would no doubt provoke among young reviewers eager to show their flashy irreverence.

I mentioned *Shanghai Express*, the dopey movie he produced with Madonna and Sean Penn. "Wrong cast, wrong script, wrong director. Where did we go right?" he asked with an amused chuckle (big, healthy teeth). You could tell he loathed Madonna personally but was too adult to indulge it on camera with a stranger, although I sensed it wouldn't have taken more than a nudge to get him going.

We talked about his ten-year-old son Dhani who, on hearing the new album, asked Dad why he hadn't written a "really good song" like "Blue Suede Shoes," to which a touchingly embarrassed Harrison replied, "He's got a point." We talked about a recent Paul McCartney sulk (again he was diplomatic) and, of course, about John

Lennon. Responding to my question about whether he now feared for his life, Harrison frowned with the authentic discomfort of a modest man and replied, "No. The truth is, I'm not important enough." I remembered that when, ten years later, a deranged fan broke into his house in the middle of the night and stabbed him. Mrs. Harrison subdued the intruder with a single downward swing with the business end of a lamp.

Our interview concluded, Harrison stayed put, chatting with the crew and producer, and then wandered off back downstairs, stopping in the doorway to talk some more. He was on his way, he said, "to meet Eric and Ringo for dinner." (There's a dinner I'd have liked to go to.)

I never met the other three Beatles. I saw a bearded Ringo once in the lobby of a New York hotel reading the newspaper, but I left him alone. You don't break in on a guy when he's taking a few minutes to read the paper. I had a few one-person-removed encounters. I interviewed Yoko Ono when she came through Toronto with a dreadful, howling album. She was very much what I'd been told to expect, a suspicious, controlling woman who interrupted the interview twice to inquire, "Would you ask that question to Bruce Springsteen?" (No, but then the Boss doesn't write songs that sound as if an animal had caught its foot in a trap.)

No one ever knows what goes on between a man and a woman and I can only assume Yoko must have been a whole lot more fun with John Lennon than she was that day with me. Sexual chemistry forgives all.

I interviewed Albert Goldman in Rome, where he had fled after publishing an ugly-minded biography of John Lennon in 1988. The whole thing stank of a publicity stunt, especially the armed guard who sat glum and bored in the corner of the hotel suite.

But I liked Goldman a lot. He was an effervescent New Yorker, a gifted phrase-maker and a wonderful conversationalist who had made a major life miscalculation: he had not understood that for a Beatles book to sell well, Beatles fans have to *like* it. At that moment in Rome, his book was number two on the *New York Times* bestseller list, but it was already falling like a lead pipe. Sensing that something very bad was coming his way, Mr. Goldman sought to anaesthetize his distress with balloon-sized glasses of red wine before lunch. It didn't help. The book ruined his career and not long afterwards he died on an airplane in mid-flight.

Near the end of our chat in Rome, though, as he was walking me somewhat unsteadily to the elevator, I remarked that the Lennon biography had taken him five years to write, which was the same amount of time that Flaubert had taken to produce *Madame Bovary*. Had it, I asked, been a prudent choice of subject matter? Given that, as a writer, you don't get those years back. He replied that he didn't know.

A few months before his death, a colleague phoned me one evening, said he had a message from Albert Goldman, whom he had just interviewed. It was about the Flaubert question. Goldman had assured my friend that I would understand. "Just tell him no, it wasn't," he said.

There have been almost five hundred books written about the Beatles. Remember, this is a group of young men who disbanded forty years ago and who recorded, in total, about ten hours of music. Only *ten hours and twenty-eight minutes*, to be precise. You would have guessed so much more! But still, by 2005, I'd had enough of them. It's not true that you fall in love only once in your life; but it *is* true that you only fall in love a certain way, with a certain absoluteness, once. And I thought that's maybe what had happened.

Sometimes I'd hear "No Reply" or "Help!" or "Don't Let Me Down" on the car radio and I'd think, That's a terrific song, but I couldn't be bothered listening all the way through, to that corny last chord of "She Loves You," or even the delicious chorus in "Here, There and Everywhere." I'd switch channels.

Then, a few months ago, a funny thing happened. I dropped into a second-hand bookstore, a grungy underground place in my neighbourhood. I was flipping through *The Alexandria Quartet*—it always reminds me of my mother—when I heard through an overhead speaker the final, dramatic bars of "When I Get Home," a song from

A Hard Day's Night. And when John Lennon got to the hook, the hair stood up on my arms.

It was barely English, but I again felt it: it was back, that odd mixture of euphoria and sadness, of being close to but still on the *outside* of something terribly, terribly important.

7

Another Day in Paradise; or, How Many OxyContins Do I Have Left?

It must have been thirty years ago when I met Nessa Cornblum. Nessa, the rabbi's daughter. She was working at the Rose Heights, an exclusive club for elderly Jewish women. She served high tea in the afternoons. Of course, she hated it. Nessa was at her conversational best when she was hating things, putting things down. She'd go still as a snake while her brain cooked with inventive cruelty—so-and-so's weak chin, so-and-so's sagging bosom—and then, finding just the right condemning phrase, when she hit the target and *knew* she hit the target, her Egyptian face slid open with a dazzling smile. Lord, she was pretty, though, that caramel skin, an almond face on which the centrepiece was a long, beautiful nose. You can talk about a woman's behind, her smell, her breasts, her fingers, she had all that, but the master-piece was her nose. It was a sexual virtue all on its own.

I was in the Bamboo, a lively, crowded bar down on Queen Street, the night I met her. I was at a table with a handful of people: Justin Strawbridge, Dexter Alexander, a medical intern, I forget his name, a night dentist, a computer programmer, an actor, somebody's younger brother (then studying to be a helicopter pilot) and a dancer from the Danny Grossman troupe. Everyone was drunk, but in a young, happy way. Nessa Cornblum was there too, sitting with a couple of young women a few tables over. She must have felt she was with the wrong crowd, that she was missing out on something, because she kept looking this way, waiting for an in, an eye she could catch, a joke she could tag, something that would let her dump her pals ("Be right back") and join us. Which she did.

I wasn't especially attracted to her, not at first anyway, which she could sense, and that, coupled with my age—I was thirty, she was nineteen—intrigued her.

I don't know who brought up Isla La Mar, maybe it was the intern or maybe a piece of music came on, but Dexter shouted, blowing a lungful of smoke at the ceiling, "Let's go back! Let's get on a fucking airplane and just *go!*"

The intern said he couldn't take a Caribbean vacation just now, the dentist couldn't either, but Justin Straw-bridge, with that rich mother of his, sat back in his chair looking like a man who's just remembered something. "Well, fuck *me*," he said, and clapped his hands. It was a small gesture, that clap, but it sealed the trip. I shared a taxi home that night with Nessa; it stopped first at my apartment on Euclid. She lived further north, up in Forest Hill with Rabbi Cornblum and her two sisters. After we said good night and I got out of the cab, she wound down the window. "Do you have anything to drink at your house?" she said.

That was the first time we were together, and it wasn't much, to be honest. A touch of theatre on her part. I have nothing against hollering and writhing and saying naughty things, but over the years I've discovered that just wanting to be there is what makes a good lover, not a 9.8 gymnastics routine.

While Nessa lay under the sheets, I poured myself a vodka, plopped in an ice cube and began to discuss, of all things, Scott Fitzgerald. The chatty gregariousness of the sexually sedated. "The reason *The Great Gatsby* feels like a longer book than it actually *is*"—here I pause for effect— "is that all the characters know each other *before* the story starts. So you've got thirty or so different relationships all going on at once." Another sip and a ruminative look out the window. (I'd said this before.) "That's what gives the book its remarkable density, why it feels like a five-hundred-page novel."

"How would you guys feel about me tagging along with you to Isla La Mar?" Nessa said, propped up on one elbow. A breast revealed.

"In what capacity?"

"Just one of the guys. But I can see you're hesitating. You're worried you're going to have to look after me down there. That I'm going to latch on to you like a lamprey."

"Did you know that lampreys almost annihilated the entire salmon and trout population of the Great Lakes?" I said.

"No, I didn't know that." Here she sat up in bed, the sheet falling entirely from her breasts, and lit a cigarette.

"And that it was a Canadian who invented a special poison which killed the lamprey larvae in the stream beds?"

Puff, puff.

"Can you imagine the ingenuity of a formula which kills only *one* species of egg and leaves everything else intact?"

"Uh-huh."

"A Canadian guy."

"So you said. But what's your answer?"

I said, "I can't look after you there. Just as long as we're clear on that."

Thinking back on that conversation now, at the age of sixty, I don't understand why I wasn't more alarmed about my future, why I didn't understand that I was dangerously close to ending up like one of "those guys" whose company you sought out in the university cafeteria but whom, fifteen years later, you glimpse in an all-night doughnut shop: he's still doing it, still talking up a storm, riffs about the second gun in the Kennedy assassination, riffs about how Brando saved Al Pacino from getting fired from *The Godfather*. But it's three o'clock in the morning, the company's different now, and he's said it all before.

So we caught an early morning flight to Isla La Mar and then took a minivan to San Agatha, a fishing village on the north coast. It had been three years.

In the daytime, Justin, Dexter, Nessa and I snorkelled in the green-water caves. At night, we drank overproof rum in the Hotel La Mar bar and saw ourselves as extraordinary people. Sometimes Nessa came to my room and got into bed without a word. Behind the hotel the foliage was overgrown and gave off a mild rotting smell and sometimes you could hear things moving around in there at night.

Then one night Nessa Cornblum didn't come.

I saw her in the hotel bar the next morning; she was having breakfast alone. The sun had darkened her skin, and sitting there in a sleeveless black T-shirt she looked so beautiful that I was scared of her.

I said, "So where were you last night, young lady?"

Young lady. You can see what I was trying to do—to get back to that zone where I had lived so effortlessly for weeks, ever since the night on Queen Street. But all that seemed like a foreign country now. And that funny, inauthentic sound of my voice? She must have heard it, must have understood what it meant.

"I got in late. I didn't want to wake you up."

"Did you fuck him?"

"Yes," she said, and returned her eyes to her omelette.

"Who?"

"Some French guy."

"The guy with the tattoo on his arm?"

"Yes," she said, relaxing as if we were on the verge of talking shop. A week before, we could have been.

"Good-looking guy," I said.

"He sure is."

I heard a voice in my head say, Do you think *I'm* good-looking?

I got to my feet. "Okay," I said.

"Be careful with yourself today," she said.

Three girls from the University of Southern Mississippi spilled into the bar. One of them had a very red face. She'd fallen asleep on the beach. Children played on the patio while their parents ate breakfast and frowned. It was a family hotel.

"Meaning what?" I said.

Nessa looked up and frowned too. It was getting worse, like a rope running through my hands. I couldn't get a grip on it.

I went up to Justin's room on the second floor, beside mine. The door was open. He was sitting on the bed, barefooted, playing a guitar the colour of sunset. Writing down the lyrics and the chord progression. He looked at me and then back down at his notebook and then quickly back up to me. "I hope you haven't fallen in love with her," he said.

"Nope."

"That could cost you a couple of years."

"What could?"

"Falling in love with her. Getting into it, getting out of it, getting over it, a couple of years anyway."

I said, "I thought we were going to the beach today."

He said, "Why don't we go down to Pamela's and buy some speed instead?" Just the idea of an alteration energized him; he put the guitar in its case with quick gestures, as though now that he had made a decision, he was afraid the opportunity to *act* on it was going to flee.

I said, "That's a beautiful guitar."

He said, "Let's go."

So we went down to Pamela's and bought three or four black Dexedrine capsules and chased them with warm beer. Pamela's beer was never cold.

Soon Dexter wandered by in a pair of cut-off jeans with a T-shirt on his head. His shoulders were covered in acne scars. I asked him where Nessa was.

"Fucking her Frenchman," he said. Dexter was the kind of friend you only keep when you're young.

We headed down the road in a Dexedrine gust, the island painted in green-gold. Looking at my friends, a day and a night of adventure ahead of us, I thought, Yes, I have managed my life well. And the proof of it is this moment.

I didn't see Nessa in San Agatha, not in the crowded street nor in any of the bars nor at a salsa dance down the beach later that same night. Which was fine until the speed began to wear off; and then my life with its gossamer achievements began to come apart like wet tissue paper.

Wandering back to the Hotel La Mar near midnight, a subdued ocean rolling in and out, I saw her coming down the road toward us. She was alone and it seemed, as she reversed direction and joined us, that I could smell something on her exquisite skin, under the coconut oil, under even a day's tropical sweat. I opened my mouth to speak, but in mid-sentence a kind of dry-tongued self-consciousness insinuated itself. Justin must have noticed it, because he shot me an irritated glance. Where will she sleep tonight, I wondered, will she come to see me?

Twenty minutes later, we were settled in deck chairs on the balcony in front of my room. Dexter was downstairs in the bar with the Mississippi girls. They were dancing to old American pop songs that had been re-recorded to a reggae backbeat. It made a cornball song like "Duke of Earl" sound snappy, even subversive. I was going to mention it, an impressive aperçu, surely, but then I thought, *subversive?* What kind of bullshit is that? And then I remembered the Toronto film critic, the guy with the monkey face who liked to talk about movies being "subversive." He fancied it made him a cut above regular moviegoers, implied a certain superior niche of sophistication.

The music stopped. We sat in the moist silence. There was a scream from the foliage behind the hotel, something had something by the throat, a rabbit maybe, but it sounded like a baby being murdered. After a while I had the feeling that they, Justin and Nessa, were waiting for me to leave so they could be alone. As if daring life to wound me, to murder me like the creature in the jungle, I said, "I'm going downstairs to get a beer." Justin said, "Could you get me one too?" Then Nessa said, "Me too."

"I'll need three hands," I said. Meaning somebody had to come with me.

"Never mind, I'm fine," Justin said.

There, I thought, that proves it. Now I have to go alone. Now I have to leave them alone.

I went downstairs and asked the long-necked bartender for two beers, one for me and one for Nessa. How long could that take? You bend over, you open the fridge, you pull out two Red Stripes, you open them and then you put them in my hands. But we might as well have been putting a man on the moon. Dexter and the girls from Mississippi were in stitches of laughter. Somebody kept saying, "My God. My *God*!"

I went back up the stairs. The dogs in the yard barked at me. They knew something was fishy. And when I got to the top, Nessa was sitting on Justin's lap, leaning forward, ostensibly to look at the moonlight but really so that her breasts could brush his lips. And it seemed unbelievable—and at the same time utterly logical—that this terrible thing was happening to me.

But then Justin said, "You got to get up, Nessa." He said it the way you talk to a thief who's got his hand, again, in your pocket. Mechanical but firm. And I remembered him at the New Year's dance at the winter hotel when I was fourteen, his hand on my shoulder, the whole room staring at me. How kind he is, I thought.

We left the island a few days later, Justin to his law practice, me to supply teaching. Dexter stayed on with an elderly Australian widow who had a place on the beach. Nessa I didn't see, but I heard later she took up with one of the Germans who owned Kaiser's Café until a hurricane blew the whole works, including the German, out to sea. But by then Nessa was long gone, taking acting classes in New York and living with the director of a soap opera.

A thousand events took place; good-natured wives came and went; I had children who to this day seem so miraculous it's hard for me to let them walk past the couch without reaching out and grabbing them.

And then one day, three full decades after that night on the hotel balcony, a letter arrived from a small town in upstate New York. A letter from Nessa Cornblum. Why just the other day she'd found herself thinking about Isla La Mar and how much fun we'd had there and oh, by the way, she was going to be in Toronto in a few weeks, the rabbi was ailing, did I want to get together for a drink maybe?

I showed the letter to Rachel. (Rule number one on how *not* to wreck a marriage: If it feels like something you should keep secret, you're probably doing the wrong thing.)

"What do you suppose she wants?" she said.

"Don't know. Nostalgia maybe."

"Old girlfriends don't look up old boyfriends out of nostalgia. They look them up because their lives aren't working out and they want to see who's still interested."

I didn't write Nessa back. I didn't *not* write back either. It just never occurred to me to, one way or the other. But then one morning a few months later, I woke up too early in our house in Kensington Market. It was the death season, end of February in Toronto, snow blowing across the porch, the sky bled colourless, litter in the gutter; a wormy dog rubbing his bottom on the frozen sidewalk. And for reasons I still don't understand (but am not surprised by) I slipped quietly out of bed (my wife sleeps like a child) and went to the head of the basement stairs. I unlocked the door and switched on the light. It smelled down there, of what I don't know, but I didn't like it, it scared me. I saw a rat down there once, and now, when I smelt that staleness, that *je ne sais quoi*, I remembered the rat, how it came scuttling out from behind an old oil painting. They have long tails, those rats. That's how you tell them from a big mouse.

There were cartons of old appointment books in our basement, letters you'll never reread, faded sweaters, electricity bills, galoshes, a fishing rod, income tax statements, a broken hammer, things like that. But there was something else as well: a bottle of OxyContin tablets. Painkillers that almost no one uses for pain. I can't remember how I got them, a lapse in judgment certainly, but I got them anyway. What can I say?

Storing them in the basement, though, in a place where the odour made me imagine rats, seemed like an excellent pre-emptive stroke. Who was going to go down there, especially in the middle of the night, the time when much of life's damage is committed? Very unlikely, too, that Rachel was going to go sorting through that stuff. And if she did, if, say, I was killed in a bank robbers' crossfire, she'd see the date on the pill bottle, blah blah blah. Even in death I wanted her to think well of me. (She'd put two conditions on marriage: no women, no pills. Who's going to contest that?)

And it worked. For the longest time it worked, so much so that for years I forgot they were there. But then that February morning, I remembered. And, like the sailors in *The Aeneid*, down I went. I gave my hands a vigorous clap (rat alarm), gave the shoe box a good kick (rat alarm), and found what I was looking for in the toe of a child's skate. I snapped the tablet in half, popped it into my mouth and chewed contemplatively. Gradually the day took on a kind of agreeable, literary melancholy, like the beginning of *Moby-Dick*. And like the guy in *Moby-Dick*, I was, indeed, setting out on an adventure, the whale, of course, transforming itself into the same entity as the man pursuing it.

It began to hail, small, hard pellets clacking against the window. A pair of Indians, pockmarked and bulbous-nosed, passed my window, pushing and shoving each other playfully. One of them had a bottle of sherry or wine, they must have just got it because they were on their way up. By night, by nightfall ... who knows? We were all going to have a nightfall.

The OxyContin clicked in another notch. I was rattling around my desk, "tidying up," when I came across Nessa's letter. I reread it. It seemed more interesting now. I thought, You've gone back to the house with the broken spine, back to your old dormitory, back to the film festival, why not go back there, back to Isla La Mar? Reflect on life's foolishness and spent passions. Romeo and Juliet on a balcony in the Caribbean. Splendid! It could be the final chapter, the payoff, the snow falling at the end of Joyce's "The Dead." How perfect. How inspired. How OxyContin!

I called an airline office. I said to myself, if they have a flight, I'll take it. I imagined the island bathed in a pool of sunshine. I saw a lagoon, a bank of cliffs rising behind it. A sailboat rocking slightly at anchor. People snorkelling at the mouth of a cave. Yes, I thought, I'll do that. I'll go to Isla La Mar, and I'll go swimming for two hours a day, I'll get a tan, I'll lose some weight, I'll go back to the balcony of that gorgeous little white hotel in the cliffs. There will be pretty girls from the University of Southern Mississippi in the bar, there will be families with small children dashing about the yard; there'll be French-Canadian couples with matching tattoos on their biceps (a beautiful race!), maybe even a pair of young men in the bar, just like Justin and me, drinking too much and raising hell. Perhaps I'd have a word with them. A cautionary note. I'd say . . . what would I say . . . never mind, I'd know when the time came.

I imagined the hotel owner's delight when he saw me. His wife emerging from the cool interior shadows, her affectionate disapproval. What naughty things had I been up to? How many years now? Fifteen, twenty since that time when I first read Tolstoy. (How Tolstoyan it *all* seemed, in fact! The cycle of people and time and places and . . . and so on.)

Rachel greeted the news circumspectly ("Been to see the doctor recently?") and slept in the third-floor guest room.

Five-thirty a.m. The alarm goes off. There it is, my plane ticket on the bedside table. I didn't dream it after all. Descending through the house like a jittery ghost (Jesus, those OxyContins leave a hell of a hangover), I arrive in the basement. I clap my hands. Was there a flicker of motion just behind the imitation Rembrandt? I look at it in the harsh light. Rachel's right: it *is* depressing. Depressing and amateurish. It may be four hundred years old, but they had bad painters then too. I clap my hands again. Yes, I'm sure of it. Something moved over there behind the book carton.

I shake a tablet into my hand and crunch it between my teeth. Is it my imagination or is the effect almost instantaneous? Horror receding like the tide. I'm down there in the basement, yes, it smells, but *voyons, mon vieux*, basements are basements. What was all the fuss about, what horror, what rat? And that painting. It *does* have a certain layered elegance.

Layered elegance.

I go back upstairs, pill bottle in hand. So much to do. Pack my fins, my snorkel, my mask; I'll wear shorts and sandals to the airport. Boy Scout maxim: travel light. By this afternoon the hot sun will pour over my back, I can hear the sweet, cognac-scented voice of Cesária Évora, I can hear the noisy chatter of happy tourists at a cliffside bar. I place the OxyContin bottle in the inside pocket of my overnight bag but then, intuitively, as though someone has dimmed the lights in a theatre, change my mind. Some things you don't risk. What if my bag gets lost in customs? What if they X-ray it and find my pills? I know better than to take a chance. I put them in my breast pocket and give it a tiny, reassuring tap.

The limo arrives; I hop in the back. Away we go. The *balcony*. I'm going back to the balcony in the Caribbean. I see Lake Ontario on my left. Grey water. Then a deserted playground; a lone jogger: poor soul, he's not coming with me today. I pull out my notebook. I must write everything down. These next few days, they may well be the most important days of my life. Scribble, scribble. I see myself a kind of Marcel Proust on OxyContin. A recorder of the minutiae of human existence. *Marcel et moi.*

The plane has barely levelled out when I order a Bloody Mary. "I love to drink when I fly," I tell the affable young couple in the seats beside me. I make notes, I go to the bathroom fifteen times, I chat to the stewardesses, more Bloody Marys, I start to watch a movie, too slow, and head back to the bathroom; there is always a cluster of people there, you can talk to them . . .

Three hours into the flight, I feel a slight sag. Hmm. What could it be? In the bathroom I look at my face. My pupils are tiny, like pinheads. I seem to have already lost weight. How great! I'll come home with my clothes just *hanging* off me.

Yet things are not quite as weightless, as compelling, as they were an hour ago. Has something happened? That woman *did* bring our chat to a rather hasty conclusion outside the washroom. Oh well, that's happened before: middle-aged women, I'm not their cup of tea, it's as if— yes, that must be it!

Reaching down into my pocket, I find a quarter Oxy-Contin (I'd razored them into portions before leaving my house) and chewed it up, munch, munch, munch, and yes, before too long, I found myself in conversation with the couple beside me: how long had they been together, how did they meet, what did their families think of "all that"? They were intrigued that anyone could be so fascinated by their life story. I had a million questions: life on a small farm two hundred miles outside of Calgary: riveting, all of it!

It was late afternoon when the minivan passed through San Agatha on the north coast of Isla La Mar. Dozens of young black men standing around the town square, bored, looking for tourists to hustle. We followed the shoreline up into the West End, the landscape speckled with paper cups, bottles, candy bar papers. The bars and cafés, the road itself, they were strangely unpeopled.

"Where is everyone?" I asked.

The driver looked at me in the mirror with an expression of practised, low-level menace. Just on the brink but not quite there.

"They don't come this far anymore," he said. He kept his eyes on me. I knew that face, the what-can-I-get-from-this-guy face.

I leaned my forehead against the warm glass. My temples ached. A fat black woman sat on a stoop in front of a shack. T-shirts and knitted caps hanging in the window behind her. It was Pamela waiting for a busload of tourists to sample her hashish cakes on the way to the Café Havana for sunset. Just thinking about her and them and it, that piddly little sunset, made me tired. The driver turned on the radio. Terrible, tinny reggae. A dying art form. No one since Bob Marley.

But what was happening? Why this sour mood change? Clearly it was time for another OxyContin. Running low. Very low. A worrisome moment. But short-lived: munch, munch, pause, munch, munch, and little by little the colour returned to the ocean, the palm trees, the little yellow shacks by the roadside. The music grew attractive hooks. Just this and no more, I thought, if I could just stay like this, all day, every day, I'd be happy for the rest of my life.

And then I was thinking about Nessa Cornblum, about her beautiful young face looking out the van window when we made this drive decades ago, the last golden sunlight playing on her features, me falling in love with her and not knowing it. How does she look now, I wondered?

I asked the driver to drop me off down the road from the hotel. I wanted a slow, sweet return. He pulled over. "Ten dollars," he said.

"I've already paid."

"No, no, this is a gasoline tax. Everybody must pay it."

"I'm not paying it."

He watched me pull my bag from the rear of the van and played his last card. "You don't like black people?"

"Not especially," I said. "I bet you don't hear that very often, do you?"

I walked slowly up the road. There it was, fifty yards away, twenty yards, then ten yards, the awning with the sea-green letters: HOTEL LA MAR. PROPRIETOR MR. DEVANE JOHNSTON. I went up the front steps and looked into the bar where Dexter had danced with the girls from Mississippi. A black metal gate with a comically large padlock stretched across the entrance. I peered through the bars. Old dresses and shirts and trousers and shoes lay stacked on the tables where Nessa had eaten her breakfast, where she had said to me, "Be careful with yourself today." The bar seemed to have been relegated to a kind of storage room for things nobody wanted. Where were they, those girls from Mississippi?

A light flickered in the interior of the hotel. I went toward it. Devane Johnston, grey-haired now, was sitting in a small, windowless office with a television set playing in front of him; the tube was blown, the screen was green and cast an unpleasant light over him. On the wall behind him was a patch of circular discoloration, a grease stain from where he leaned back to rest his head.

"Devane?" I said. He was asleep.

"Devane?" Eyes opened in a large black face.

"It could have fallen from the ice truck . . ." he said. He was still dreaming.

"Do you remember me, Devane?" He rubbed his features with a big hand and looked at me again. I could hear him breathing through his nose.

After a moment, he said, "You're still here."

"Well, it's been a while, for sure. But yes, yes, I'm back." I listened to the silence of the hotel. "Where are all your dogs?"

"Somebody poisoned them."

"You didn't get any more?"

"No. No more dogs."

His eyes returned to the television screen. A soccer game.

"Who's playing?"

"I don't really know."

We sat for a moment, the green stick figures dashing about on the screen. He picked up the phone and dialed a number. He said my name and then something else in patois. Then he repeated it more forcefully.

"Is that your wife, Aiesha?"

"Hmm."

Good, I thought, his wife was always fond of me.

"Where are the other guests?"

"There aren't any."

I inquired about a slim, rather wry waiter who used to work there. Gone to the States with an American girl he met at the hotel. I inquired about Devane's mistress, the one he used to fool around with while Aiesha was teaching school a few islands over in Port-au-Prince.

"Still good." I asked him more questions, but I soon noticed that the ball never came back over the net. He didn't ask where I'd come from, how long I'd been in town, even if I was going to stay at his hotel. And this was something of a disappointment. I had told my children perhaps too many times about the famous Hotel La Mar and its commanding proprietor. The former burly police officer who had quit the island's force, immigrated to England, earned a degree in engineering while raising a family of four, and returned to San Agatha to build the hotel with his own hands. A hotel that had been for many years a favourite getaway for middle-class Canadians and their young families.

To be honest, I'd rather imagined that he might be curious about what I'd been up to during all these, what, twenty, twenty-five years. Apparently not. I mentioned a trip we took once, Devane and I, in his pickup truck to the south end of the island to buy a new refrigerator. No, he didn't recall that. I reminded him of that time we carried that poor boy from Kansas City to his room (sunstroke). A blank there too.

"Do you still keep a gun in the safe?"

Someone scored a goal and from the little green screen came the rolling, slightly sickening chant of an English soccer match.

"Can we turn off the TV for a second?" I said.

"Of course."

I gave it a final shot. I reminded him of Justin Strawbridge and told him the story of the Duane Hickok killing. It appeared to have been the only thing I'd said so far that caught his attention.

"But he's good now?" Devane said.

"Well, he's out of jail if that's what you mean."

"Well, good. That's what I'm interested in hearing." I found this remark puzzling. Was I being too self-congratulatory? Taking too much relish in the misfortune of an old friend?

"I'd like to spend a night or two here, Devane. Can I have my old room, the one upstairs with the balcony facing the road?"

"That's got air conditioning now."

"It'll be a cool night. I won't be using it."

"The air conditioning is twenty-five U.S. extra."

I diverted my eyes to disguise my embarrassment. "Shall I pay now?"

A skinny man appeared in the doorway. He was wearing a pair of jeans several sizes too large secured by a leather belt that was also too long and hung like a snake down the front of his pants. The skinny man, Lee, carried my bag off into the night; I could hear his feet going up the stairs to the room almost above us. To the room with the balcony.

I started to leave. "Oh, Devane. Do you remember Nessa Cornblum? The girl with the beautiful nose?"

"Nessa. . . ?" he said, and tilted his head to the side. "The one that give you such hell?"

"Yes, that one."

He chuckled and slid a few inches down his chair, settling his hands on his stomach.

"Did she ever come back?"

He thought for a moment. "Yes," he said. "Five or six years ago. She was looking for someone."

"Who?"

"A French guy."

"Did she stay here?"

He thought for a moment, resting his head against the greasy circle. "Just one night. Then she disappeared." I could hear the croaking of night frogs in the foliage behind the hotel. "She must have found him," Devane said, and chuckled again.

Was he putting it to me?

"I'm sorry about your dogs," I said, rising to leave.

"I know who did it, but I can't prove it."

Going down the hall, I could hear the soccer game. Like dead men swaying.

I went to the front of the hotel and sat down on the steps. What had just happened? Who was the man in the windowless office? My "old friend" Devane? Oh dear. How could I ever have been so naive? Or was it that he'd just gotten old, an old man with a dying hotel and he didn't give much of a shit about anything anymore, including his wife to whom he had spoken on the phone in a flat, cold voice, the way islanders talk to their help. Then I remembered that she hadn't bothered to come out and say hello.

A hand touched my shoulder. I jumped. It was Lee, the man who had carried away my bag. "Do you want me to send a girl to your room?" he asked.

"A girl?"

He nodded.

"Where would you get a girl from, Lee?"

He pointed to the far end of the hotel, an ugly two-floor cement addition that looked like a motel in Florida. A clothesline with a few ghostly shirts hung in front.

"You mean they live on the *property*?"

He nodded.

I said, "When did this happen?"

"When did what happen?"

"How long has Devane let whores live in the Hotel La Mar?"

Over my head, I heard a television go on.

"That's Larry," he said. "From Texas."

"Just me and the girls and Larry upstairs?" I said.

"Yes, sir." This mechanically, as if he were repeating the obvious. Then he again looked down at me with a pair of shattered eyeballs. "So I fix you up with a lady tonight?"

I went upstairs and lay down on the deck chair on the balcony in front of my room and tried to think about Nessa and Justin and that night under the moonlight. How it had felt, the sight of her on his lap, as if a huge metal pipe had come swinging through the darkness and hit me right here, in the chest. The personification of everything you feared . . . But the deck chair was filthy and I had to go back inside and get a towel and wipe it down. Nobody cleaned anything anymore at the Hotel La Mar.

I had just settled back down when I heard flip-flop footsteps coming up the stairs. It was Larry from Texas. He was a bland-looking man in a green shirt with bright yellow bananas on it; my age, mid-fifties, with a white plastic nose shield. With that thinning fair hair, he must have been especially sensitive to the Caribbean sun. We chatted for a bit. I found his southern ease comforting. Maybe we could have a drink sometime, I suggested.

"Wish I could," he said, adjusting his baseball cap and squinting down the road, "but I'm going home tomorrow."

He took off his sunglasses, revealing a pair of extraordinarily blue eyes. "I don't want this summer to be like last summer."

"I beg your pardon?"

But he didn't answer. He pointed those bright blue eyes down the road as if he were hoping someone would appear just at the bend, coming this way, but knew at the same time that no one would. It stayed with me for a while, that remark "I don't want this summer to be like last summer." There was something mildly sinister about it, something that whispered *Pay attention*. But pay attention to what?

It was dark by the time I set off down the road. I walked along the top of the seawall; I put out my arms like I used to in the old days. (I was a lot thinner then.) A wind had come up; the waves crashed against the wall and for a few minutes I was happy to be there, to be back. But I could also feel something just behind me, a patch of dark, heavy air; as if I were keeping just ahead of it. In the corner of my vision, a rodent scurried for cover among the sea grape bushes.

I took another OxyContin and gradually, moment by moment, it seemed that the night was sharper, the stars were sharper, the air dense with meaning and mystery. I stopped in front of an empty discotheque; red and green lights whirled around the dance floor like a madman with an axe.

I went all over San Agatha that night. I found every-thing thought-provoking (on the way up), sweetly sad (coming down), amusingly irritating (down further), *un*-amusingly irritating (descending, descending), a persua-sive argument for capital punishment (flatlining). Then, a fresh Oxy, ground up between the teeth, things change again. I'm feeling warm and understanding about the Third World situation, at home with the panhandlers and spongers and drug dealers. Live and let live, that's what I say!

I took a taxi to the end of the beach; I took a taxi far into the cliffs. I walked and walked and walked, and how I saw myself and how I saw my life depended always on where the drug was. Somebody told me there had been a high sea that very morning and a California girl had been swept off the cliffs and out to sea. And someone else said she must have done something to bring on such misfortune.

Near four in the morning, I was crossing the yard toward the stairs to my room when I saw a black girl come out of a doorway at the back of the property. She must have been waiting there. Skinny as a snake in a purple shirt and jeans, she seemed to float across the grass to-ward me. "You want a back rub?" she said. And I thought, All I need to ruin my life is just to nod and let her trickle back up the stairs behind me, past Nessa's balcony, into my room. And like a man watching a subway hurtle down the shaft toward him, I thought, I could do this. I could step off this platform into the path of this train and no one would ever know that I only did it because I *could*, because it was so *obviously* the wrong thing to do.

When I got back to my room, I fished through my bag, took a sleeping pill and came back out and lay down on the deck chair on the balcony. After a while I began to taste almonds and I knew that the pill was taking hold, that soon it'd pull me under, slowly, happily drown me. And my last thought was: What a frivolous young man I was.

I slept for I don't know how long. A car door slammed and woke me up. A woman shouted my name just outside the window; a sudden puff of wind blew into the room, the curtains thrashing about like spirits taking flight. I parted the venetian blinds and looked toward the far end of the property. Someone had taken down the clothesline; the shirts lay spread-eagled on the grass. A pair of head-lights flashed on; a red car rolled slowly down the drive-way. Music from inside. Passing under my window I saw the dreadlocked driver. There was a girl in purple beside him. She glanced up toward my curtains. I stepped back. The car moved out of sight down the driveway and then I heard it turn and accelerate toward San Agatha.

I went out onto the porch; you could see the twinker-ing lights of the grand hotels across the bay. Couples asleep, families asleep, safe in their beds, together. The reassuring swish of air conditioning in the background.

The pills had worn off and I felt myself slipping into a kind of frightened sadness, a lament really, a *life* lament for all the time I'd wasted here as a young man. For the terrible hangovers, for the pointless love affair with Nessa Cornblum, for the pointless suffering that it involved. But there was something in addition to all that, a sinking realization that for years and years, even into my early thirties, I had persuaded myself that getting drunk in the Hotel La Mar bar and talking about Rimbaud was some kind of achievement.

"I don't want this summer to be like last summer," Larry had said. Yes, I understood that now, too.

There was a chill in the air. I crossed my arms and rubbed them. It was just getting light, the first goldfish traces of daybreak across the bay. Something moved at the edge of my vision. I turned my head slowly. It was as if a giant cocoon had been woven during the night, a cocoon at the end of a string. What sort of a beast could make a thing like *that*? But it wasn't a cocoon. It was a man hanging by the neck from a clothesline. His shoulder turned slowly toward me. It was Larry. Larry, slowly turning in the morning breeze. A rooster crowed. And then the dogs woke up.

The police were still there when the taxi came. They were upstairs in Devane's living quarters. I thought I heard the sound of laughter. I'd forgotten: Devane Johnston used to be a cop.

I didn't bother saying goodbye. As we pulled away, the last thing I saw of the Hotel La Mar was the whore in purple from the night before. She was standing on the balcony outside Larry's room with his nose guard on her face beneath a pair of pink, heart-shaped sunglasses. There was a different woman inside Larry's room. You could see her through the open door. She was holding up a green shirt with bananas on it, trying to figure out if she liked it or not.

The taxi bumped slowly down the road, past Pamela on her stool, past a group of fat white men in Harley-Davidson muscle shirts looking for their younger bodies, past those sad little roadside conch shell stands, past a golf course, past a bandaged madman gesticulating wildly on the Green River bridge. A few minutes later, on a stretch of highway, a hot wind blew through the cab, like a stranger expelling a lungful of breath in your face. A sign loomed up on the left. YOU ARE NOW LEAVING SAN AGATHA.

A child in a pink dress looked quickly over her shoulder and disappeared down the embankment.

8

The Pigeon

A friend of mine, a beautiful Chinese Canadian, recently discovered that her ex-boyfriend— she'd been the one to call it quits—had been sleeping with another woman the whole time he was with her. She staggered around for a week or so, stunned. How could this have happened? How could he have come home at the end of the day and asked, "What's for dinner?" when, only an hour previously, he'd been banging some undergraduate's head against her dormitory headboard?

And why had he told her *now*? Probably, I suggested, because he hoped it might spark some terrible jealousy that might, somehow, win her back. Or to get even, perhaps.

Quoting an old Chinese proverb, my friend said, "If you want revenge, dig a grave for two."

Well, yes and no (although I certainly didn't say that then). But she came to mind the other day, my Chinese friend, when I went down to the CBC broadcast centre.

There was talk about my participation on one of those hokey television panels, this one on why Jane Austen novels make good movies. I was waiting for the show producer when I spotted René Goblin in the lobby. He was older now, his dreadlocks greying, his pink gums still flashing when he smiled. And still sporting those black, thick-framed glasses that made him look like an ousted African dictator. (Why are those men always so ugly?)

I'd forgotten. A while back, René Goblin had gone from being a staple book reviewer at the *Globe and Mail* to the host of an avant-garde, after-midnight radio program. He was at a table with young people, producers I guessed, talking in that deep, avuncular voice and showing, every so often, those appalling gums.

It surprised me how much pleasure it gave me to see him. Sometimes, contrary to what my Chinese friend says, revenge really works out, really cleans the barnacles off the bottom of the boat. This isn't an especially attractive story, but it's a true one. And to be quite honest, just thinking about it still makes me feel good.

It was my fourth novel; I'm not whining, no one forced my hand, but I'd worked very hard, had rewritten the thing seven times from scratch, from page one. It was just about to come out and I was very anxious indeed. The *Globe and Mail*, Canada's newspaper of record, had wounded me three times in a row with bad reviews. René had done an especially nasty hatchet job on one of them.

The fact that he'd rung up the paper and volunteered for the job gave me the unpleasant sensation that he was gunning for me and that he might well do it again. Make no mistake: people believe what they read in the newspaper. Worse, after a while they start to think that *they* thought it.

So I did something I'd never done before. I went to see the *Globe*'s book editor, Avery Lynch. He was a pink-faced man in his late fifties who fancied himself, *la grande littérature* aside, quite the ladies' man and detoured the conversation in that direction whenever he could. But I wasn't there to talk about women. "I've gotten wonderful reviews," I explained (cretinously), showing him (cretinously) clippings from New York, Vancouver and Miami newspapers. "But for some reason I've been getting panned over and over again in your paper. I can't seem to get a good review in my hometown."

"Really?" he said, looking at the clippings and then up at me. He mentioned the name of a woman novelist considerably more gifted than I and added, "And we've panned *her* three times." He rounded his eyes with affected surprise.

I went on. "I'm particularly concerned about one of your reviewers. René Goblin."

Avery nodded encouragingly.

I said, "The truth is, I don't think René ever got enough girls in high school and I think he's never forgiven me for the fact that I did." Prior to opening my mouth, this had sounded plausible, even reasonable.

"Really?" Avery said, amused. A hint of mockery? I wasn't sure. But I hurried to explain myself, and as I heard the slightly breathless tones in my voice, I felt myself sinking, my point getting lost in vanity and silliness.

"Well then," Avery said, a smile still animating his pink features, "I'll have a word with René. And if he *does* have a problem with you, we'll make sure to get someone else."

"Who?"

"Just somebody else."

"Maybe *you* should review it," I said. "I'd be very grateful—"

Avery cut me off. "Don't worry, we'll handle it at this end," he said, and went on seamlessly to the subject of a young actress we both knew (she wore a slim gold chain around her neck), referring to her as "my lover." I nodded judiciously, connoisseur to connoisseur. What a dope, I thought.

"Did you, by the way?" Avery asked, rising from his chair to shake my hand (short-sleeved white shirt and tie) and, in so doing, to signal our "meeting" was at an end.

"Did I what?"

"Get enough girls in high school?"

I considered my answer carefully. I knew what he *didn't* want to hear. "Does one ever?" I said.

He gave a short bark of laughter in which you could feel the relief. For a second there, I think he was torturing himself with the image of a teenage boy (me) between the legs of a teenage girl, her jeans hanging from the bedpost.

It was an unorthodox thing to do—you're not supposed to make that kind of personal appeal when you've got a book coming out—but I left Avery's office and headed uptown feeling lighter in spirit, as if, by vocalizing my concern, I had removed a small, insistent headache from right behind my eyes.

So, fine. The book came out; there was a launch party at a bookstore, followed by a gathering at my apartment. My editor came, so did a few old friends and their pals, along with my girlfriend Molly Wentworth, her parents and embittered brother who taught at Stanford but wanted to teach at Harvard. (Academics are even nastier about each other than writers.) I looked around the apartment every so often; there were twenty or thirty people there, including both my ex-wives—M., hawk-featured and somehow "in charge" (she had prepared the food), and Catherine, my son's mother, a lanky actress who liked everyone and was therefore liked back by everyone. It was, I thought, a pleasant party, everyone talking to everyone.

And yet, as I moved from group to group around the room, I had the feeling that I was waiting for something. I couldn't engage in conversation, not with anyone; each little bit of chit-chat felt as if it were holding me up, stopping me from doing something important. But what was it?

I couldn't help but notice, though, that Avery Lynch from the *Globe and Mail* wasn't there, and that struck me as odd. Usually he went to these things. He liked to turn up with his girlfriend with the little chain around her neck and talk to people with his arm around her. She was quite a bit younger than he was, his "lover." Code for, "I'm fucking her," of course.

Near three in the morning, as the guests cleared out— a drunken Englishman lolled about on the couch impersonating his rich mother—I started to gently dismantle the party, taking the empty wine bottles into the kitchen, covering the cheese plate and so on. Using a book from my bookshelf, an especially mediocre Canadian novel that had been reviewed with excessive generosity a while back, I began to cap the flames on a set of small pot lights which sat in a row directly above the couch. But I'd had a few drinks, I lost my balance and knocked one of them over; molten candle wax dribbled down onto the couch. I even got a splash on my pants. It was a disproportionately shocking accident. Fixable but somehow, it seemed, malevolent, as if the spilled wax symbolized the consequences of a careless life catching up with me. Of a life lived *incorrectly*. Why hadn't I pushed the couch from beneath the candle's reach before trying to extinguish it? Wasn't the choice of an ungifted writer's novel as a snuffing instrument a gesture of unattractive spite? Was I being punished for it? Had I not, in fact, knocked over a candle at almost exactly the same spot a few years earlier?

Still worse, the spilled wax seemed like a bad omen for my new novel, and Avery's no-show at my party assumed an even more sinister tone. The remaining guests, noticing the spill, made sympathetic groans, but no one took it with any gravity. An actress with a haggard face (she really should quit smoking) suggested a hot iron and a brown paper bag; a playwright with big ears who had spent entirely too many years giggling (in an irritatingly high pitch) at parties and sleeping with women not his wife mentioned a brand name and giggled again.

The next day, I came down the stairs into the living room more hungover than I should have been; it was the kind of hangover you get from drinking to get a flat evening airborne, from "forcing" it. Thinking back on the party, though, there *had* been something rather sinister about it. But what? My book had come out at a difficult time of year, March break, people away on holidays, so several friends had been unable to attend. And that had given the evening a sort of *uninhabited* feel. Yes. True. But that wasn't it.

Cleaning up the living room, rinsing the wineglasses, dumping the appalling cheese tray (I couldn't stop noticing the candle-wax stain on the couch; it seemed to occupy the centre of the apartment), I was left with the feeling that I hadn't had a single satisfactory conversation all evening long. I'd start talking and be interrupted; start again and be interrupted again. But what else could I do? I was too old to be a guest at my own party.

All day I wondered about the upcoming review in the *Globe and Mail*—it was scheduled to appear in the Saturday edition—and I kept returning, like picking at a blister, to Avery's no-show. And to René Goblin with the black-rimmed glasses. I had a sick feeling, you know the kind, that I *knew* what was going to happen, that in spite of my visit Avery was going to get René to do the review. Just to show me what happens when a writer wanders into his office and starts telling people what to do.

On the other hand, somebody at the party had told me a young woman writer, a noodle-armed sexpot everyone had a crush on, was launching *her* new novel the same night as mine. *How To Be A Girl*, it was called. Bound for success, from the title onwards. So maybe Avery, "player" that he fancied himself to be, went there instead. To give her a sniff, so to speak. Mind you, you couldn't fault him for that. I'd met this girl once; she was so erotic with her skinny arms and little-girl voice that I'd daydreamed about her for weeks . . .

Anyway, where was I? Yes, the review. I'd thrown the party *before* the review came out instead of after so that if things went poorly I wouldn't have to contend with long-faced people showing up at my door or pretending they hadn't read it or, worse, feeling sorry for me. The whole thing was a nightmare and at some point that afternoon, my hangover clicking in a notch, the stain from the candle wax accusing me every time I walked by the couch, I decided that I was never, ever going to write another novel. That it wasn't worth the stress on my nervous system. No, I'd become a high school teacher instead. Drink too much at night and jack off in the staff washroom to images of Italian students in wet T-shirts. A much healthier existence, that!

Around eleven that same night, I fled my apartment as if it were on fire and hurried to my favourite newsstand (I'm a superstitious man); the early Saturday edition wasn't in yet, but hang on, what's this? A broken-down fellow in a long coat drifted along the sidewalk with an armful of newspapers. He was working the bars. "Paper. Saturday *Globe*," he said in the tone of a man who knows no one is listening but makes his announcement anyway.

I shouldn't buy it from him, I thought; he looks like bad luck. But then impatience won over—it always does—and I bought the paper, giving the man a large tip as a way, I hoped, of neutralizing his effect. From there, with an escalating heartbeat, I took an expensive taxi to the house of Catherine, my second ex-wife, across the bridge in the Greek part of town. It was a cold spring night; the creek beneath the bridge glinted malignantly. I found myself thinking about my poor cousin who, when he discovered his wife was having an affair, threw himself off this very bridge twenty years earlier. What was his name? But why think about that now? Still, it was a hell of a way to kill yourself. He'd done it in the middle of the day, just pulled his car over to the side of the bridge and hopped over the railing. Down, down, down he went. What must he have thought about, plunging into the creek like that? And his wife! I saw her at the funeral with their three children. She took my hand softly and whispered in my ear, "It's all right. He's better off now."

Better off now? How do you figure that? Then I remembered the playwright with big ears giggling at my party; what an unpleasant racket! Why was a man at his age still giggling?

I knocked on the door and waited; Catherine appeared behind the glass, peeking out with a kindly smile. That long face, those lovely brown eyes. Like a nurse or a mother; a woman for whom wounded men call out on the battlefield. I handed her the *Globe and Mail* as though it were a police warrant.

"Do you want me to read it here?" she asked. "Or go upstairs?"

"Upstairs. Please."

It was a small house with her eccentricities everywhere. A piano she never played; odd ornaments here and there. Edwardian dollies; tasselled lamps. A pair of bright yellow rubber boots she had bought for two dollars at a yard sale. (Our son, Nick, had implored her at an early age to please never wear them when picking him up after school.) But it was a comforting home, as if a benevolent ghost drifted nightly through the rooms dusting their contents with cozy powders.

I heard Catherine's footsteps cross the floor over my head and come to a stop in her bedroom at the end of the hall. Then silence. My heart crashed, then crashed again. I got to my feet. I paced the living room, picking up this and that, a yellowing aerial photo of the Saskatchewan farm where she grew up, a beaded wallet, a Joni Mitchell CD; I turned them over in my hands, unseeing. What was taking so long? But on it went; not a sound, not a movement.

And then steps, rather slow, moving across the ceiling, followed by her voice at the top of the stairs.

"It's a disappointment," she said.

"Who wrote it?" I shouted, as if the answer might make me feel better, might stop the spinning, downward plunge.

"René Goblin," she said in a voice trying for irony. But she wasn't an ironical woman and it didn't quite hit the right note.

"René Goblin? That's impossible."

But of course it wasn't, and everything fell into place with a ghastly clank: Avery not coming to my party, my premonitions, the cripple selling the newspapers, the nasty creek winding beneath the bridge, the giggling playwright.

Sometime after midnight, I took an expensive taxi home from Catherine's house (twenty dollars), flung open the front door to my apartment, went straight downstairs to my basement locker (where I hid them from myself) and took a sleeping pill.

Don't believe that old adage that a bad review is supposed to ruin breakfast but not lunch. A bad review can spoil a good deal more than that. This one, this ugly-minded pigeon shit (I'll kill that motherfucker!), made me feel as if my novel, only days out of the gate, had already a stain on it and that every time I looked at it, like at the couch, I would see only the stain. It made me feel as if everyone in the world had read the review—people on the street, people going by in cars, people looking out the window of a hairdressing salon—which produced in my body a sensation of physical distress, like being in a horror movie. No matter where I turned I couldn't shake it. I had spent three years writing the book, weighing this sentence, that sentence, and now, or so it seemed, it was all over in the space of time it took my ex-wife to go upstairs and say, "It's a disappointment."

And such cruel phrasing (why did I keep rereading it?), the implication being, in every sentence of the review, that I had taken on a complex subject (sexual obsession) and had simply lacked the talent to pull it off. "He's just not that good," Goblin had written as the review's final, condemning axe stroke. And indeed, because all writers, including René, suspect that they're "just not that good," those words activated an already existent agony. My beautiful book, my beautiful book. Ruined by someone who spent an hour and a half reading it. I simply couldn't shake the appalling, almost electrical waves of shame and hurt and rage and injustice. Because it had been, after all, a lovely book. A lovely book! (Look at that! Already in the past tense.) I'd had such hopes for it. Only somebody who didn't like me could dislike it. Or so I reasoned.

Yes, yes, I understand—and understood then—that a creative life is neither made nor broken by a single review. Who remembers the critics (and there were many) who panned *The Great Gatsby*? It had happened before, over and over and over again. I was also old enough to suspect that after a certain age you can't distinguish between good luck and bad luck (not until you see how things play out), but this was still a hard slap in the face. This terrible poison coursing throughout my body.

To distract myself, to cool the fireball in my stomach, I flipped to another section of the newspaper. But I wasn't safe there either. It was a day designed to torture me. For there, in front of me, was the prize-winning short story from this year's national competition. It started thusly:

Blame force of habit, if you like, or early-onset misan-
thropy or just the simple rules of coincidence: But none of

*this ever would have happened if he hadn't got up before
dawn to beat the holiday traffic.*

I stopped reading and said to no one in particular—
for there was no one else in the room—"This is precisely
the kind of bullshit writing that wins prizes in this country." I looked at the paragraph again. *"Early-onset misan-
thropy"?* What's that? And what's the guy beating early
morning traffic for? Let me guess. He has a cottage. *Who*
has a cottage these days? It was middle-class twaddle,
the kind that only matrons in Canadian book clubs enjoy.
Jesus, this was my audience.

"Who has a cottage?" I bellowed. It was like those terrible television shows that have people gathering around
the water cooler. *It never happens.*

I bent forward and underlined the paragraph in clumsy
red ink, but then, not liking the look of that either, I hurled
the paper onto the floor.

There were many things that irked me that morning: a
neighbour's radio, the ghastly clawing of pigeon feet outside my bedroom window, a car alarm going off. "Fix that
fucking alarm!" I screamed out the window.

Then I took another sleeping pill. Pills are never a
good idea, especially for me, but I thought, to hell with
it, I'm not interested in feeling like *this* all day. So I fished
around in the basement again until I found the frosted
vial in my winter boot, gave it a shake (a reassuring swish-

swish) and popped a green tablet into my mouth, swallowing it dry.

Lesson number one: Sleeping pills don't always make you sleepy. Sometimes they can make you very busy indeed; and about an hour later, red-lipped from having downed a delicate Burgundy I'd been saving for my daughter's university graduation, I sat at my computer and wrote an imprudent note to the pink-faced Avery Lynch, a letter which concluded with the bewildering demand that the next time he, Avery, threw a party, he might clean up his house beforehand, this last bit referring to a gathering I'd gone to at his house three years earlier where, by ten o'clock, there were no clean glasses left and a grubby, fraternity-house feel hung over the proceedings. Alarm bells sounded in my head, but when the moment to hit the Send button arrived, they were too muffled to make their case, and off went the note.

I must have passed out, because when I woke up it was dark outside. I set off to find René Goblin. A self-consciously *with-it* asshole like René would probably gravitate to College Street on a Saturday night, one of those appalling *boîtes* with young men dressed in black who let their cellphones ring in restaurants. Self-important little pricks to a man. Yes, that's where René Goblin would be, explaining in tones of quiet condescension (I was certain) why, try as he did, he simply couldn't restrain himself from giving my novel a public smack. "The bottom line,"

I could hear René say, "is talent, I'm afraid. *He's just not that good.*"

A furious revenge movie ran and reran in my thoughts as I hurried up through Chinatown, turned left at the fire station and headed along College Street. "I'm not going to eat this one," I said, and moved closer to the bright ring of lights. The plan: to walk into the bar, situate René, proceed directly to his table, get his attention and deliver a mighty slap across his face. Which would knock his glasses clean off. Those stupid, affected glasses. Deliberately ugly. Glasses that said, *Aren't I interestingly unattractive?*

But I didn't find René that night. I poked my head into a handful of shadowy, candlelit bars that I'd quit going to a dozen years before. At The Butter Bar (stupid name), I asked the bartender if she knew René Goblin. Yes, she did. Had he been in tonight? No, he usually comes in Sunday for the jazz.

For the jazz. How perfect. How René!

"Tell him this guy is looking for him." I wrote down my name on a coaster and handed it to her.

Then I went home; I don't remember taking my clothes off. But the next morning I awoke with the sense that something horrible had happened. It was very early, the sky still red behind the tree branches outside my window. Blood-red. What have I done? I wondered, and then I recalled the taxi ride to my ex-wife's house, her kind eyes, the apology in her voice at the top of the stairs. How glad I was, though (it washed over me in a wave of grati-tude), that I hadn't found René.

The morning wore on, and as it did, the nausea—and fury—returned. Knowing better but striking a posture of embittered nonchalance, I slipped downstairs for more sedation. And this time it worked. I curled up under my covers comforted by the surety that I would fall asleep. It was as though by taking the pill I had been guaranteed passage through a safe and welcoming valley: sweet vege-tation, pastel birds, a clear stream glinting in the sunlight. Just before I slipped under, I remembered writing the email to Avery Lynch. Fuck him, I whispered to the cur-tained room, and fell asleep. It was a little after eleven in the morning.

Looking back on what happened next, I can't quite pinpoint the timing of events. Those several days remain in my memory like the pieces of a broken jug. I woke up; it must have been early afternoon the same day, the sky bright blue. I spotted the newspaper on the floor with its violent red underlining and it scared me, as if I were drift-ing toward a black iceberg, that I needed to do something concrete to order my life, to inflict a kind of structure over things which might prevent me from being further wounded. I took a letter that had been lying on the din-ing room table for weeks, an unimportant cheque to an unimportant creditor, and thought, That's it. I'll mail the cheque. And again I caught sight of the melted candle wax on my couch. And again it frightened me. It seemed to say, *You have let things go too far.*

I'll take care of that too, I thought.

But first the letter. I put it into my shirt pocket and went onto the porch and unchained my bicycle. I noticed my fingernails were dirty and I stared at them, puzzled, for a moment. I never have dirty fingernails. I rode up my street, turning onto a cinder pathway that traversed the park. I could see the red, sturdy mailbox between the trees. It was a concrete goal, the beginning of mending myself, and in that and in the comforting sound of the cinder under my tires I could feel a kind of relief, quite involuntary, come over me—the worst was over—when out of nowhere a pigeon ran in front of me; it came from the left, small-headed, pink-eyed, scurrying like a fat man trying to catch a bus. I felt a rise and fall in my back wheel as if I'd gone over a small speed bump. I looked over my shoulder, afraid of what I was going to see. The pigeon, its feathers scattered, was flopping back and forth on a broken wing, pulling itself across the walk toward a child's sandbox. But why is he doing that? I wondered. Why is he trying to get over to that sandbox? In his wake lay a trail of *under-feathers*, delicate, like a kitten's fur. And the sight of these feathers struck me as more horrible than blood.

Taking the envelope in my hand, my fingernails filthy, I dropped it into the red box and took another route home.

Back in my living room a few minutes later, I avoided the window that faced the park. "What should I do?" I said out loud. I thought of calling Catherine. Asking her. (God, if it's not ex-girlfriends, it's mutilated birds. How much must an ex-wife put up with?) But it was my mess, my problem. I knew I should go back to the park, find the pigeon and put him out of his misery. Bash his head in with a rock. "But I can't *do* that," I said, again out loud, aware that my mouth tasted very bad indeed. You can't smash a pigeon to death in a public park. People will see me. They'll think I'm murdering a pigeon because I don't like pigeons. Somebody might even want to fight with me.

But that wasn't it. What I was afraid of, really afraid of, was the *violence* of doing it, the blood, the mashed-in head. In response to an unseen audience, I said, "I don't have the stomach for it. I am not of that world, the violent world." And while I was saying this I remembered René Goblin and the plan to punch him in the face. "I am not of that world," I said. And in the calm that followed, I felt that I had been spared, that a dreadful presence had come and stood very close to me, and then gone away.

I washed my hands and cleaned my fingernails. When I got to the park, I saw the pigeon lying very close to the wall of the sandbox, the very wall he'd been in such a strange hurry to get to only seconds after the wheel had crushed him. But he didn't look in such bad shape now; a bent wing, yes, but no blood. I thought, He's made it this far. Maybe he's going to survive. I shouldn't kill him now, not with him making it this far. But why, I wondered, was the bird staying so close to the wall? He was pressed right up against it. What was *there*? As I turned to go home, I saw a cat stealing across the grass towards me; but it wasn't until later in the day that it occurred to me why he was moving like that, so low to the ground, and why the pigeon had wanted to get so close to the wall.

And again I thought about phoning Catherine. I stared at the phone, I put my hand on it and I rehearsed my story. Then I dialed her number. It rang and rang and then her voice-mail message came on, the voice of a woman whose first impulse is to like strangers and trust in their innate decency. I caught a glimpse of myself in the mirror, my head seemed too small for my shoulders, and put down the phone.

I started a book tour, going from city to city across the country. But everywhere I went, it seemed as though I could smell Goblin's hateful review. I could feel it in the poorly attended public readings; I detected it in a journalist's tone of voice, even in his greeting when he shook my hand. Even the book itself, the actual physical entity, began to acquire an almost electrical charge. Like an ungrounded refrigerator.

I gave a reading in Vancouver. Two hundred empty seats. A scattering of people, even a woman wearing a garbage bag with armholes. Three elderly ladies waited patiently near the front, all with copies of my novel in their hands. I tried to flee. I was seconds from a clean get-away when a local television crew turned up. Taking me by the arm, a young producer steered me toward the octo-genarian table.

"I'd like you to read to them," he said. "Don't worry, I'll shoot it close." When I saw it later, it looked as though I was reading a bedtime story to senior citizens.

I woke up the next morning in a rage. Staring out at the beautiful harbour below my hotel window, a jogger making his way bouncily along the footpath, I wondered if I was going bonkers. Was I going to allow this guy, this Goblin, to spoil every moment attached to this book? Every moment attached to the act of writing *itself*? Could I not impose some kind of control over these feelings, this obsession with a thoughtless review? Why, I wondered, does it seem that flattery is always a lie but a condemna-tion—a condemnation has the ring of truth? My brain teemed with snakes. *Unless you act, unless you do something about René Goblin, you're going to feel like this forever—*

Eighteen months passed. One afternoon I was walking home after a visit to the dentist. It was a grey, overcast day in the garment district, the sidewalk busy with peo-ple coming from and going to lunch. I stopped to do up my shoelace, and just as I looked up, there was René Goblin passing on my right. He glanced over and kept going, an easy stride, looking at this and looking at that in the store windows. There was a touch of the theatrical about it, as if he were performing for me, as if he were saying, Yes, I recognize you, and your unpleasant feelings about me are of so little importance that, see here, I can even take time to look in shop windows.

As if I had come across someone who had abused one of my children years before and gone unpunished, I found myself calmly, murderously alert. And the notion that he had said such terrible things about my book, had been *recreationally* cruel about something that mattered so deeply to me, that he assumed—by that gait alone—that not only had he gotten away with it but that my feelings on the matter, then as now, were not only unimportant but possibly even amusing, threw fresh gasoline on what had been, until a few moments earlier, a small if insistent back-burner flame. But I am not one to forget a slight.

I also knew that if I waited, at some point René was going to find a pretext to stop his leisurely advance up the sidewalk and look around. I was sure of it. He crossed a small street, still no backward glance, and then came to a halt in front of a large window. It was a bedding store, mattresses and sheets and pillow slips. I could tell by the angle at which he was standing that he was, in fact, staring at my reflection in the glass. Those ugly black frames on his glasses. As if I were being pulled by a cord, with the conviction that I was absolutely in the right and would never ever be able to draw a breath again unless I did this, I walked straight over to René Goblin and smacked him across the face with an open hand. The black-framed glasses fell to the sidewalk. So did René.

Then a strange thing happened that even at the time I knew I would never forget. Without looking at me, René pulled himself into a doorway; and in that gesture there was something appallingly vulnerable, sickeningly so, and I found myself thinking about the pigeon hurrying to the fence, even with a broken wing.

I meant to say something; even as I swung I had imagined a crisp, perfect utterance, but now it escaped me. I stood looking down at René, frightened, ugly René. I picked up the glasses and offered them.

"Don't," he said, pulling further into the doorway. Realizing that I had now entered into something that was not easily or perhaps ever fixable, I placed the glasses gently on the sidewalk.

I didn't see him again for a long time; and, life being life, other things, other concerns moved into the rooms that René had so thoroughly occupied. Sitting under the big skylight in the CBC broadcast centre, I realized, seeing him across the room with that young crowd of producers, that what I was feeling was not guilt or shame or regret, but delight. René Goblin was not a place, not a film festival hospitality suite, not an old dormitory, but for

a while he was certainly an arena of vulnerability. I remember wincing when I saw his name in the newspaper
or heard somebody mention his name in conversation.
Until I smacked him, that is. After that, I felt okay about
the whole thing. I still do.

9

The Alligator under the Bridge

It was a brief moment of prosperity. I was forty-three, I was the host of a harmless little television show on the arts; guests came and went, actors and writers and musicians flogging their novels, movies, CDs and what have you. It was like the provincial branch of an advertising agency that disguised boosterism as "arts journalism." But it paid well and satisfied the cravings of my almost insatiable vanity.

On the recommendation of a colleague, I rented a vacation house that summer on the island of Sanibel off the coast of Florida. A snobby little enclave where, in those days, the only non-whites you saw had garden rakes in their hands. To the delight of my children—my son, Nick, then aged eight, and his naughty sister, Franny, fourteen— I hired a stretch limo to drive us to the airport; it had a sun port in the roof from which, as we drove up the street, they poked their beautiful heads.

In the Miami airport, we rented a white Mustang convertible and then, with the top down, the air conditioning on Los Angeles–style, children in the back seat, sound system thumping reggae, we beetled across the breast of Florida; we drove through swampland, ate an American lunch (food for ten) and swooped, hair flying, along a sea-scented coastal highway. We stopped for a moment in St. Petersburg to take a photograph of my son standing in front of the same strawberry hotel where I had posed for my mother's camera, seagulls wheedling overhead, almost thirty-five years earlier. (How odd, how unimaginable the way one's life unfolds. How strange these two photographs look, side by side: me, chicken-chested with big ears, my son, a cockier stance, his deep-set Slavic eyes gazing warily at the camera.)

We took a wrong turn in Fort Myers and drove through a tough neighbourhood, bars on the windows, crumbling sidewalks, boarded-up stores. My daughter, her blond prosperous hair fluttering in the breeze, waved at three black teenagers picking their way across a parkette. A middle finger rose from the discarded candy bar wrappers and sunburnt grass.

"Stop," Franny hollered from the back seat. "I want to *speak* to those guys!" We continued on.

Three blocks later, American-style, we found ourselves in a different kind of city. Snappy little cafés with ferns in the window; gay men in shorts with tans and crisp biceps and white, white teeth. One of them walked a small, pug-faced dog. We drove past a grocery store a block long and then turned onto a magnificent bridge; there was the smell of the ocean again, salty and mysterious, a smell that made me nostalgic for a time in my life that had never actually occurred. A white deep-sea fishing boat pulled into harbour. In the rear-view mirror I caught a glimpse of my children in the back seat, the late afternoon sun on their faces, and I remember thinking, I will never be this happy again. (Happily, I've thought this before.)

We drove along the coast of Sanibel, our little island, turning here and there, through a small town with a video store and then into a driveway shaded by heavy, overhanging trees. It was a white house with big windows which, to my surprise, looked as good as its photograph. You went out the back door, crossed ten yards of hot sand, skirted a jacaranda bush and then crossed over a gently arching wooden bridge. A small alligator lived under there; you could see him in the morning, half submerged, slit-eyed. After that, the beach. Women with shirts knotted at the waist drifted along the water's edge. Short bald men who looked like Picasso walked in pairs. On the blue horizon, a freighter hung motionless, like a child's painting.

I unpacked my bags; I unpacked *War and Peace*.

In the afternoons, while my children splashed like seals in the pool or made noisy, messy lunches for themselves in the kitchen, I underlined and made notes and tried to write like Tolstoy. (That book never saw the daylight.) But I was happy; we were all happy.

Three days later, Molly Wentworth, my girlfriend, arrived and she was *not* happy. You could see it the second she got out of the taxi, a strained smile on her face. (She was already aware of something but, because she was so young, she didn't quite recognize what it was.) Molly was a blond, stick-figure girl, pointy-featured, a television producer whom I had fallen narcotically in love with. In her white jeans and T-shirt, she had seemed, I remember, so full of beans, so *engaged* and excited by life. An up-for-anything girl. You want to get in the car and drive to Buffalo tonight? Sure! I looked over at her once in a movie theatre, her short hair, her sharp chin, her lovely eyelashes, and felt almost alarmed at the pleasure just the simple fact of her *being* there gave me. How lucky I felt. (I was old enough to no longer take love for granted.)

And for a long time, indeed, it *was* lovely between us. Then gradually, like a photograph in a developing tray—only in reverse—her face began to darken. It seemed as if the rooms she moved through darkened too. At the time I didn't know what it was. (I didn't understand the nature of accumulated scar tissue.) You could feel the tension coming from her young body, a troubled smile, a mechanical cheerfulness, almost like a child who is trying to stay out of trouble. And when she laughed—near the end there—it was, I now realize, an expression of relief that a storm had passed her by. In a word, I scared her. Not with blows or harsh words, but with a suffocating anticipation of disapproval. And eventually she stopped loving me for it.

"Are you sure you put it there?"

"Yes, absolutely certain."

"Then where is it?"

It occurs to me now that that's how you lose a woman. She doesn't need to find you in bed with a boy; it's merely an accumulation of jagged little pricks and careless bruisings until she catches herself at a turn in the stairwell or stopped at a red light and realizes she doesn't want to be there anymore. This person who once so adored you that she lied to her friends, or went on three hours' sleep to spend the night with you, prefers a life without you.

I saw her once emerging from the side door of our apartment building in Toronto. I hid behind a tree. I couldn't face the nervous exchange that was only yards away.

"Right, then, see you tonight?"

"Sounds good."

"Okay."

"Everything okay?"

"Peachy."

"Peachy. . . ?"

Sometimes, in our house on Sanibel Island, I caught her staring out the window at the ocean and I wondered, What is she thinking? My children, Franny and Nick, raced around the house doing laundry, making snacks, quibbling, videotaping each other. But there was Molly, in the centre of all this liveliness, and absolutely alone.

We were coming home one night from dinner at a fish restaurant on the other side of the island. It was already dark; the island a jewel of windows and dock lights; somewhere there was a lighthouse. The car roof was down; I turned on the radio; a country and western song came on. The children rested their heads against the back of the seat and let the wind and the moonlight play over their faces.

We drove slowly past our white house.

"Can you drop me off here?" Molly said.

"I thought I'd drive around the island," I said. "It's such a beautiful night." A night as beautiful as Natasha's night in *War and Peace* when she calls her cousin to the window to see the stars.

"Here's fine," Molly said. And she got out of the car. I waited a moment until she walked down the driveway; the porch light clicked on; she went up the stairs, this little stick figure in white shorts put her key in the lock and then, without a backward glance, went in.

The three of us drove on. The children tactfully silent. Children miss nothing.

Molly returned to Toronto for unspecified "family obligations" a few days later. I stayed on. But some nights, after a day of trooping around Sanibel with my children, here for hamburgers, there to the video store, I experienced an inexplicable sense of agitation, an unwilling sortie in that zone of frightening *private* thought (frightening because of its incommunicable privacy). The arena where nineteenth-century Russian novelists are so incomparably *true*.

I woke up night after night at four in the morning. With only the ghostly whisper of air conditioning in my ears, as though I were in an airplane flying through the night, the rest of the passengers asleep, I felt that I had committed a terrible act for which I was about to be punished. But I couldn't put my finger on what I'd done. I had that teetering, out-of-time feeling you have in those first waking seconds the morning after a cherished lover leaves you. You know something is wrong, but it takes a few seconds to remember what it is.

But what had I *done*? My children were asleep, safe and healthy in their beds. I had a job, a few friends, my ex-wives loved me, I didn't have leukemia. I hadn't written bad cheques or, like the young Rostov in *War and Peace*, lost a sickening amount of money at cards.

What *is* this horror? I asked myself.

Was it death? Was it Molly?

I wandered naked through the dark house. I looked in on my children: Franny, her bony arm thrown over her forehead as if protesting; her brother, chin pointed slightly upwards; he had kicked off his sheets and lay sprawled in his blue boxers. I covered him up. Kissed them both on the forehead, first one, then the other; and the sense that I was there to watch over them, that they slept such untroubled, exposed sleep because they knew they were safe, made the horror momentarily recede.

I slipped open the glass doors at the back of the house; you could hear the ocean from here; *boom*, a pause; then *boom*. I was going to go for a walk in the cold sand, but just out beyond the jacaranda bush I felt the presence of something that unsettled me.

What *is* this horror?

A horror of losing a life that I cherish? That someone will take it away? That circumstances will take it away? That I will do something to destroy it? (It takes years to build a good life, a long weekend to wreck it.) Or is this an *inherited* horror? A scared-of-the-dark horror: a million years of things trying to eat you, a sensation that is not easily dispelled by turning on the light?

The Russians (naturally!) have a name for this bout of middle-of-the-night terror. They call it Sparrow Nights.

But what could it have been? In the years that have ensued, whenever these Sparrow Nights might occur, I have wondered again and again if I am (forgive the California tone of this) receiving a coded warning from the future, that a black train is coming up behind me; that it will catch me looking down the tracks in the *other* direction, wondering, Hmmm, what *is* that racket?

Or was it something less operatic, less *Russian*? Is it simply how your body feels when you're over thirty and can no longer sleep like the child in the next room; when, as Leonard Cohen puts it, you "ache in the places you used to play"?

I stood for I don't know how long in the open doors of our rented house; it was getting light over the ocean, a dazzling orange sky melting into pink melting into blue. How verblessly beautiful the world can be sometimes, I thought. Almost enough to make you believe in God.

To no one's surprise, except mine, Molly left me several months later.

It happened on a Sunday. Dreadful things always happen on Sunday. Molly and I were in the living room of our small apartment and I was talking when her beautiful eyes filled with tears. "I can't live here anymore," she said. I put a consoling arm around her. "Then you mustn't." I was bluffing, for sure. I had rehearsed this very speech, it was part of my straighten-up-and-fly-right approach, a no-nonsense "buck up" to a young woman from an older man. One bad decision followed on the heels of another. Which is to say that I then went to a movie, leaving her alone in the apartment.

A gloomy winter darkness was settling over the city when I made my way back home across the park a few hours later. I saw Christmas lights blinking cheerfully in our apartment. She's changed her mind, I thought, changed her mind and decided to stop whining, to "buck up." I hurried up the stairs in a state of palpable relief, put my key in the lock and yanked open the door. Soft music played on the radio; the kitchen was immaculate, plates stacked in the holder, counters scrubbed. I went into the bedroom. Her cupboard was empty, the hangers still clinking. She must have put on the Christmas lights to lessen the impact of her departure.

At four o'clock the next morning, I rose from my bed like a madman, looked at myself in the bathroom mirror, looked at her empty cupboard again (no, I had not been dreaming) and lay back down in a fever. A sinister daybreak stole over the neighbourhood. Everything looked different: the mailman more coarsely featured; vicious children on their way to school. A pair of black dogs copulated on the front lawn.

Near noon, I called Molly's father, a sweet-natured man, at his dental practice. Yes, he knew where she was and gave me the name. A girlfriend's house. More dialing. Yes, she was there. (Everyone so kind this morning; was that, I wondered, because they wished me well or felt sorry for me and wanted to cushion the blow?) Molly came to the phone. Trying to find the right tone of jollity, I said, "Boy, I bet *you* had a pretty nutty sleep last night."

Except she had no idea what I was talking about. Molly came over that evening; she looked ravishing, newly minted in a way that terrified me. I could feel my confidence ebbing away. I suggested it would be "all right" if she wanted to come back. No? I proposed marriage; I offered to give up drinking; I did everything but hang upside down from the shower rack by my feet. To all of which she said, sweetly, no, thank you.

Gradually, over the next few days, it occurred to me that this was a nightmare from which I was unlikely to awaken any time soon. I could feel it in my stomach, even before she could manage to say the actual words: I'd lost her. (Was *this* the black train from my Sparrow Night?)

Crazed with insomnia and not eating, I went to a psychiatrist M. recommended. (Perfect, your ex-wife looks after you when your lover bolts!) He was a vaguely Asian-looking man with a gentle manner and a handy prescription pad. "What does your gut tell you?" he said.

"That she's not coming back."

"Then you're probably right," he said, and scribbled a scrip for some little green pills that gave me about fifteen minutes' relief before they wore off. I burnt through a month's supply in a matter of days.

Not long after (by my standards, anyway) Molly took up with another man, a tall, failed musician (I add forgivingly) who worked at the same television network I did and had a desk not twenty feet from mine. Which meant that I saw him daily. Every time I turned the corner and headed through the newsroom to the elevators, I passed his desk. He worked in a position considerably beneath mine, but somehow, from the second I learned he was fucking my precious Molly, that seemed like a card in his favour: the signature of a rebel, of a man who wasn't afraid of non-achievement. Whereas for me, my stature seemed like an indictment, a proof of my conformity, as if I had made a team that wasn't worth making; had joined a golf club that seemed prestigious but once you made it inside revealed its mediocre trappings.

When I glimpsed the musician in the morning, my chest seizing like a car engine, I thought to myself, He has just left her bed; and a whole series of not very original but excruciating images would start up in my imagination. I saw her doing this, doing that. Sometimes, as I passed close by him in the cafeteria or in the queue at the elevator, I thought I could smell her on his skin.

It seemed to me that there couldn't be a God, that no one could be so spiteful as to have my Molly leave me for—of all the humans on earth—a man who sat a few desks away. I know what you're thinking, reader. You're thinking, That's the point, dummy. That's *why* she did it. But I don't think so. I think Molly chose him because she liked him; I don't think, to be fair, she gave a second's thought to where he sat or even worked in the early days of their love affair; and that when she did, she probably would've preferred for things to not have played out quite that way. I think Molly was glad to be rid of me, like an oppressive darkness standing over her, but I don't think she wanted me to suffer. She simply wanted *away*.

But my God, coincidence can be cruel. One day, it was a late November afternoon, darkness growing over the city, grains of snow pelting soundlessly against the windows, I was drifting around the building up on the eighth floor; I was safe up there. *He* never went there. But as I was walking down a line of desks, producers busy, getting ready for the evening news, running footage in editing suites, scrolling down computer screens, I passed the desk of a young woman, Evelyn Dunne. I'd forgotten she worked up there. She had cream-white skin that erupted occasionally and a large, attractive bosom which was hard to take your eyes off, even when you were hearing about an earthquake in Mexico City, 25,000 people dead. ("Shall we wait till it gets to 50,000 and *then* lead with it?") She was effervescent and friendly and always wore black.

I knew—because I'd seen them together early one morning in the flea market—that Evelyn had "dated" the musician. In fact, I'd met them together once. Molly, who had known him as a child, introduced us, a foursome on the summer sidewalk, no one suspecting how extraordinarily full of surprises life was and that these surprises awaited all four of us just down the road.

I passed by her desk, my head down. I wanted to avoid a conversation, with its inevitable adrenalin-prompting questions. "No, I don't know what Molly's up to these days." Or, "Yes, I have lost a little weight." I needn't have worried. Evelyn was talking on the phone and had other concerns. I heard her say in a plaintive voice, a voice that vibrated with upset but tried to pass itself off as high-spirited, "But you never *call* me!"

In an instant, like being mugged from behind, I realized she was talking to the musician; that she'd been dumped; that he'd stopped coming around, stopped phoning because he had a new girlfriend. And that new girlfriend was Molly. My Molly.

It didn't seem to matter where I went in the city; I couldn't escape from the horror that she was gone (how I missed her body, her skin) and that she was fucking another man in all the ways that she'd fucked me. People repeat themselves, especially if it works.

I thought sometimes, imagining them together at night, that I was going to pass out from the pain. And that this pain might be doing actual physical damage to my brain.

Some afternoons, I'd look over; he had his long feet up on the desk, he was chatting breezily on the phone (while I looked on like Count Dracula), and I knew he was talking to *her*, that they were, as a couple does, exchanging the high points of their day, making a plan for the evening; joking perhaps about a little bit of naughtiness the night before. I was afraid, too, they were talking about me, a whispered, "Oh yes, he's right over there. Looking pretty wrung out if you ask me."

I expect my suffering, for she knew me well, knew I was suffering, gave Molly no pleasure. But I felt it gave *him* pleasure, the sight of me worn thin with jealousy and sleeplessness. I thought this because I'd thought that way about other men when I "took" their girlfriends away. (As if you can take away a happy woman!) But how ungenerous I'd been, how smug, how quietly convinced that superiority (mine) had taken the day. And now I was paying for it. Bent over, a sharp stick up my bum, I'd been forced to my knees, the object of public (I felt) ridicule (everyone knows!).

I entertained thoughts of death. I wished him dead. No, to be honest, I wished *her* dead. Not O.J. Simpson–style, but a car accident, a brain tumour, something where I might turn up at her funeral with a long face (I saw myself in an Edwardian jacket) and commiserate with her parents in a clear, sincere voice. A voice that sought to pass off relief—he's not fucking her anymore—as sincerity.

I often thought, getting up in the night to change my sweat-soaked T-shirt for the third time, I thought: I'd be better off dead than feeling like this. I looked at my gaunt face in the bathroom mirror, the light too bright, and daydreamed of catching a terminal disease. Not to punish her. But as a release for me. An honourable release. You can despise a man for committing suicide but not for dying of a disease, I "reasoned."

That February, I woke up too early every morning; it was just getting light. It was always getting light. How will I get through the whole day? This endless, interminable day, a series of grinding, meaningless, rewardless exertions. I wandered naked around the apartment. I imagined her in her bed with the musician, I saw the light come through their curtained windows, I saw them stir slowly from sleep, I saw them . . . why go on? There were mornings when I hurried over to Catherine's house (my second ex-wife now for six years), when I banged on the door at six-thirty in the morning, when I stood in the darkness of her bedroom saying over and over, "I can't stand *another* day of this . . ."

"Get in bed," she'd say. "Get in bed and go to sleep."

"I can't sleep. I cannot endure the horrors of what I see when I close my eyes."

"Then let me sleep," she said softly. "I have to sleep."

How could an ex-wife be so kind, so gentle? How lucky I was.

I waited three months for Molly to come back. I sat on the end of my bed looking over the park that lay just beneath my window; there were children who came there to skate every morning; in the afternoon, teenagers played ball hockey; at night, when the lights overhead came on and washed the ice in a surreal brightness, couples, some-times with a small child in a snowsuit between them, skated around and around and around; at midnight, the lights went off, *poof*, the ice fell into darkness; and then little by little, a dreamy oval came back into focus under the moonlight.

I lost twenty pounds. I considered a conversion to Christianity—anything to make her come back. I burst into tears in restaurants, went home with a transvestite by mistake. Why did I never, not once, call her up and say simply, Please come back to me? It wouldn't have done the cause any good, I know that, but it would have done *me* good, just to say it, just to have the courage to put out my hand, knowing it was going to get slapped and returned empty. But I was afraid to hear the actual words, their finality. When a woman leaves you, I've learned, she tends to have done her homework before she hits the door. The sound you hear is the click of a vault closing and you're on the wrong side of it.

As winter faded into spring, dark patches appeared here and there in the ice below my window and no one came to skate there anymore.

Going through the laundry cupboard one night, I was looking for a fresh pillow slip, I came across—it almost burned my fingers—an old birthday card from Molly, a yellow card with a big happy face on it. Finding a love letter from a woman who once loved you and doesn't anymore is a special kind of agony. I opened it up: "How I adore you," she wrote. "How lucky I am to have met you . . ." It was unendurable to read the words, the glow they gave off. And to then remember that she no longer felt that way, that I hadn't seen her for months, that she was in another man's bed now, or having breakfast with him or listening to the radio in the morning while she and he got ready to go to work. She, who had so loved you, was gone forever.

Another Sunday. Having exhausted my sleeping pills and tranquilizers and painkillers for fabricated toothaches, I awoke, again, at a brutal hour, the bright yellow sunlight stabbing at me through the curtains. I threw back the covers, rumbled through the unused clothes drawer, found a pair of sweatpants (a brief nod to Molly's fitness regimen), put them on and, without even brushing my teeth, fled my apartment as though evacuating an earthquake. I went jogging—jogging of all things!—over to Queen's Park near the Parliament buildings. Around and around I ran, the sun getting brighter, the park deserted except for the lunatic and the homeless and the heartbroken, when I heard, I swear to God I heard, the sound of large feet clomping behind me, getting closer and closer and closer. I looked over my shoulder—it was him! The musician, out for a morning run, and running, I might add, with a younger, more ferocious, happier stride than mine. He passed me on the left without looking me in the eye and

charged ahead. Sorry for me, perhaps. Showing off. Exhilarated after another night of sexually ravaging my
Molly. Who knows? But watching him pull ahead, Jesus,
talk about a metaphor, talk about God giving you a kick in
the groin just when you're trying to stumble to your feet.

There was no escaping. I saw him all day: his bony
elbows, sleeves rolled up, casual, artful; his long musician's
fingers. Ugh. When I left the television studio, I hurried
through the spring half-light, the air fresh, couples everywhere, toward a bar on Queen Street. I had an hour or so,
a reprieve. They're having dinner now, I'd think. They're
having dinner with friends: frivolous laughter. *Ha-ha-
ha, ha-ha-ha.* Foolish jokes. Jokes that she wouldn't have
made or laughed at in my presence. (Part of the problem,
perhaps.) *Ha-ha-ha, ha-ha-ha.*

Morons.

But then, as midnight approached, gong, gong, gong,
I had a sensation of a worn leather belt tightening around
my chest until I could barely breathe. They're going home
now; they're climbing the stairs to his apartment, they're
going in the door; he goes to the bathroom, clank, she goes
to the bedroom, she stands there for a second, *thinking
about something* (what is she thinking? is she thinking
about me?), and unbuttons her shirt, thoughtfully (she is
thinking about work tomorrow, not me at all), and drops
it on the chair; absent-mindedly unhooks her bra, her

jeans drop to the floor; she picks them up, folds them and crawls into bed as the bathroom door opens and he comes into the room . . .

Was this, I wondered again, what lay at the heart of those Sparrow Nights on Sanibel Island, the anticipation of some unknown pain in store for me? The alligator under the bridge eyeing me expressionlessly as I crossed over for my morning swim?

Somewhere near two in the morning, sitting on the edge of my bed, staring into the park below, I turned my eyes toward the glowing clock on my bedside table. "They're asleep," I thought. And for a few moments I felt relief. Almost as if I'd gotten over her.

On it went.

And then one day I woke up thinking about something other than Molly. And that, as we all know, is the beginning of the end. You wake up thinking about a letter that needs mailing, a bill that should be paid, a toenail that needs clipping, and that is the beginning of the end of her. Time speeds up again; and after a while there are other people in your bed, other voices on the phone. And when you see people in the park under your window, they aren't an accusation of *anything*; they are, again, just people in the park. On it goes.

Eleven or twelve years went by, and one spring evening my wife, Rachel, and I and our young daughter were driving home from somewhere when we passed the park, the one right under the window of my former apartment. It was Victoria Day, the grass teemed with parents and children. Dogs chased each other through the darkness. We pulled over and got out. Fireworks erupted, people cried out and clapped; our daughter, a thoughtful baby finger in her mouth, fastened her huge blue eyes onto the spectacle. A Roman candle sparkled and hissed and shot forth a cascade of blue and green and orange exploding balls; and as they reached their apex and began a slow descent to earth, in their light, I saw Molly; she was at the far edge of the park just under my old window; and on each side of her, at shoulder level, stood a boy—they were her twin sons. One of them turned his head up to her ear and whispered something and she smiled and wrapped her arms around him and hugged him. And I tried to remember that winter and that awful spring, sitting on the end of my bed, looking down at the very spot where she now stood with her children; and instead of feeling nothing, which I expected, I felt the most extraordinary sadness, a truly deep grief, not from wanting her back, but for how much I had loved her and how sad I'd been, and how, even though we shared a bed for six years, we had never spoken again.

And then another burst of vermilion exploded above their heads and she started across the grass with her sons; they passed in front of us, not ten yards away, my wife, my daughter staring at the sky, clapping, Molly walking by, over to the far side of the park, when she reached her hand behind her back; her small hand hung there for a moment and then I swear she wriggled her fingers. It was barely a wave, if that's what it was at all. Perhaps she was scratching her back. But I don't think so. I think it was a little wave that said . . . I don't know what it said, hello maybe, goodbye maybe, or simply, yes, yes.

Then she was gone, and that night, for the first time in years, I had a happy dream about her. I don't remember what it was, but when I woke up, it seemed as though we had just spoken and it had gone well.

10

The Big Circle

ollywood, 2008. We are walking along Sunset Boulevard, my twenty-two-year-old son,
Nick, and I. It's early evening, the sky an
eggshell blue; traffic is picking up steam; it's Friday night.

We are in town, the two of us, on a book tour, the book
in question being an account of how, with my permission,
Nick dropped out of school at sixteen and spent the following three years watching movies in the living room
with me. It's a strangely popular book, more popular, in
fact, than anything I've published in twenty-five years,
probably because it's not about me, but about how much I
adore my son. No one can resist a great love story.

We've been on the road for three weeks now, in and out
of New York a couple of times, Chicago, Miami, Houston,
Santa Monica, San Jose and now Hollywood. This is our
last stop before we go home and return to our separate

lives. For my part, I'll be sorry when the tour ends, not that I need to be interviewed anymore but because I'll miss his company. We travel well together. It'll be a long time before I go through airport security without thinking of him in his stocking feet, the agent waving a metal detector up and down his tall body. It's peculiar the things one's memory grasps onto.

I am telling Nick about that awful summer almost forty years ago, how I washed up here in Hollywood after Raissa Shestatsky dumped me. Back then I believed you could get over a woman by leaving town, and I hitchhiked three thousand miles to find out that the contrary is true. What can I say? I was twenty-two years old.

Nick loves these stories, not because he's a sadist, but because it makes him feel less alone to know that someone else has suffered from love and survived. He's quite the ladies' man, and like all ladies' men he has taken some harsh and surprising knocks along the way. "Nothing is free," I tell him, "especially sex."

When he was younger, he used to roll his eyes when I said things like that. I'd say, "I tell you these things, Nick, because I want to spare you some of the horrors that I have visited upon myself." He'd put on his listening face—he was a nice kid—but didn't buy it. Nowadays he listens more soberly, less sure of himself. Which, when it comes to suffering, is a good thing.

"Every time you sleep with a woman," I say, "an invisible rope flies between your ship and hers. And you never realize it *until you try to break away*."

I point out a small grassy park off to the right. During the summer of 1969, on the run from Raissa's ghost, I slept there almost every night for three months. I was rousted by the police only once, the night after Charles Manson's satanic little playmates issued forth from a desert ranch to butcher Sharon Tate, her unborn baby and three companions. It happened not far from here, I tell Nick, right up there in those glittering hills. He finds this intriguing, that his father was alive for such a historic event. "I was around your age," I say, and you can see him ponder that. How, he is wondering, could it be that my father was *ever* my age?

He wants to hear more about Raissa: was she beautiful, yes, did she ever come back to me, no, did she have a happy life. She became an elementary school teacher, I say. I can feel his dark eyes scanning my face for condescension.

"You can be happy *and* be an elementary school teacher," he says. Nick, in that moment, is not his father's son. He is, by disposition, sweeter than I am; he likes things to work out for people, for their stories to come to a happy end. It must be from his mother that he inherited this goodwill. From his father he has inherited . . . other things.

We sit down on the park's only bench, cars pounding by on Sunset Strip. A warm, twinkly evening. The sky pink now.

Looking around the tiny park, Nick says, "I bet you never imagined this—being on a book tour with your son—when you were sleeping here forty years ago."

To which I reply, "I believed that fate was going to give me everything *except* the one thing I wanted. Which was to be a writer."

"I feel that way sometimes," he says, "but not about writing." A pretty girl walks by the edge of the park; he watches her walk away until she crosses Sunset and turns down a leafy street.

"Did you think you'd ever get over Raissa?" he asks.

"I thought about her every morning for two years."

"Every *morning*?"

"That's how you know you're over someone. When you catch yourself thinking about something *else* first thing in the morning."

He ponders that. "Two years is a long time," he says in a voice that says, that'll never happen to me.

"Not in terms of a lifetime, it isn't," I say. "In the terms of a lifetime, it's barely a chapter. Well, maybe a bit more than that. But you don't really get over a woman until you find someone you *desire* as much as you did her. And then it doesn't seem to matter how long it took."

"Because you're so relieved?"

"It just doesn't matter anymore. And it's hard to remember why it did."

I can feel him sliding into a dark mood. He's thinking about that girl again.

I direct his attention back to the Hollywood Hills rising up in a bank of lights and darkness. "You see those hills over there?" I say. "One night, some shirtless kid with little jug ears came by this park; I was sitting right over there on the grass. I think he was from Oklahoma. He had a tiny vial of LSD and, using a dropper, just like an ophthalmologist, he gave everyone in the park a little drop of acid right in the centre of their eye. He said it worked faster that way. Everybody did it. So did I, but not first. I waited to see what was going to happen.

"It was very pure, very strong LSD, and I ended up wandering shoeless along Sunset Boulevard, alone—you should never take acid alone—and I had a 'vision.' Corny as it sounds, I saw Raissa's face up in those hills, a huge, weeping Madonna-like Raissa. I thought I was going to fall down, right there on the sidewalk, and die. Just from the agony of it."

"From the *loneliness* of it." He's seeing himself in the story now. "You and her and now *this*."

"Exactly."

He leaves his eyes on my face while the rest of the film unspools in his imagination. "But you got over her eventually?"

"Yes."

"And had a good life?"

"We're here, aren't we?"

For a while, neither of us says anything. The traffic passing by dreamily. I find my thoughts drifting to other places: an island in the Mediterranean, a brick boarding house, a hospitality suite, a high-windowed apartment, a dance in a winter hotel, a patch of grass in Los Angeles, places where I'd been knocked flat. Places where, if only I could have seen down the road—to this night, this bench, this park in Hollywood—then . . . then what? An irrelevant question, perhaps.

But what is this sensation I'm feeling? It is another thought intervening. It occurs to me that this revisiting of my past has something of the salmon swimming upstream to it. All along I've been thinking I was writing a book about a guy who goes back to places and people and music where he has suffered and sees them from a fresh perspective. But sitting here on Sunset Boulevard with my grown son, it occurs to me that that's not what I'm doing at all; that what I'm doing is getting ready to die. Putting my psychic and emotional affairs in order. The goal of all philosophy, Montaigne says, is to learn how to die properly. And that, I realize, is what I'm doing. It's not a morbid thought. I'm not talking about next week or next year. I'm simply saying that I can feel the wind has changed and that my boat is gradually turning toward harbour.

I don't believe in an afterlife. Well, I do and I don't. There *is* an afterlife, but not in the religious sense: it's just that you don't die *all at once*. It's more like a light bulb cooling off after you click off the power: things just slowly fade until they match their surroundings: no God, no other plane of existence, just a slight delay in the drop into oblivion. So here we are.

Nick has lit a cigarette but, knowing that I hate him smoking, holds it discreetly by his side, out of my sight. He, too, is lost in thought. I wonder what about. We imagine we know our children, but they too are a vast, dark continent, in which the glow of city lights here and there lets us know that we are over land, but little else. Is he thinking about a blond girl with a silver stud in her nose (they say she's in law school now)? A Vietnamese beauty who used to wake him up in the morning? On warm summer nights you remember those girls. He takes a deep puff from his cigarette as if he's intuited my thoughts.

"How did you live?" he asks. "When you were here, in the park?" A deflective question. He has gone somewhere private and doesn't want to be asked about it.

"Doing that," I say, pointing at a skinny kid who is walking between the cars up and down the centre of Sunset Strip with a batch of newspapers under his arm. The L.A. *Free Press*. "You made ten cents a paper, plus tips."

"I bet you were good at it."

"Not bad. Not bad at all."

And we retreat again into private silence. I find myself thinking about Clarissa Bentley, the girl on the Ferris wheel. Just thinking about her makes me smile. A bad apple, that one, my Clarissa. I don't know if she went to trial for that opera house scam, I wasn't interested enough to find out. But executive swindlers are out of fashion these days. So who knows, maybe she got hers. We all do, sooner or later.

Bill Cardelle, the handsome boy she left me for? Not so long ago I was invited to a Christmas party at the house of a woman I used to work in television with. And guess who turned up with a plump wife? Bill Cardelle. And as the night wore on, the butlers serving martinis and champagne and hors d'oeuvres, one of the hostess's teenage children put some music on, too loud of course, but before the damage was stopped, I saw old Bill start to move, just the chin, then the shoulders and then he broke into a little two-step, it was over in seconds, his hand perched on his wife's shoulder, his tummy hanging over his belt, a pair of tasselled crocodile shoes moving light as a feather beneath him. Damned if he didn't still have the moves. He could still do it.

I'm thinking about Dean now, my older brother. Not such a happy story. He has joined a religious cult and lives in a boarding house somewhere in the Annex. I haven't talked to him for many years, but sometimes I see him, white-haired, walking along the sidewalk with a kind of aggressive nonchalance. Always alone, no woman, no friend with whom to share a casual dinner. I am his only living relative now, and sometimes when I see him I can feel my heart contract in anguish and I long to approach him, to put my arms around him, to remind him of those years when we shared the second floor of that white house in the country, me at the end of the hall in the room with the cowboy wallpaper, him in the middle with his maroon radio from which issued the echoes of a ghostly baseball game. But I have done that before, and it has always come to a bad end. So I don't anymore.

My thoughts move to M., my first ex-wife. And I feel myself on the verge of shaking my head, partly with admiration, partly with exasperation. She still sours after her third glass of Chardonnay. More and more things set her off: Republicans, the police, anti-smokers, Catholics, our present prime minister, talkative taxi drivers, corporate lawyers, anyone who finds fault with our daughter. Talking with her after that third drink is a bit like trying to land a fully armed fighter jet on the deck of a heaving aircraft carrier. But for all her prickly eccentricities, she is wildly popular. Rich women give her their fancy, worn-once dresses; lawyers don't charge for their services (or at least don't expect to be paid). She continues to be invited everywhere. You'll see her at the gala party every night of our city's film festival (where by the end of the evening everyone annoys her). I don't know how she does it, but she appears to have the capacity to be eternally forgiven. Unlike her ex-husband.

And look, here's Catherine, the beloved mother of the young man beside me. She is performing in a play right now, I remember, but I forget the title. Ibsen, I think, whom I don't especially care for. It seems that as she gets older, Catherine grows more beautiful. In fact only the other day I was in a restaurant having dinner and I saw a woman, stately, elegant, rise from a table on the far side of the room. And I thought to myself, My God, who is that beautiful woman? She looks like the queen of a small European country. And it was Catherine. She'd been there all along.

Justin Strawbridge, my childhood soulmate, wanders out of the Los Angeles fog and stands, it seems, right in front of me. I didn't see him for many years after he got out of jail for the shotgun killing of Duane Hickok. But then one day, not so long ago, I did. He was coming out of a copy shop in Toronto. He had a thick pile of manuscripts in his hands. Poetry, I imagine, reams and reams of poetry. He has grey hair now, tied at the back in a long ponytail. He fancies himself, I think, an outlaw, and given that he's killed someone, I suppose he is.

Strangely enough, I saw an email from him posted on my website not ten months ago. The first communication in twenty years. It was a sad, meandering note, full of nostalgia and a description of his life that only someone who has accomplished little—and suspects it—would write. He wanted to know if we could get back together, play some music like in the old days, maybe even head off to Jamaica, "have a blast." He wrote a few more times, but I never responded. Some great love for him died that day in the dandelion field.

And after him, God knows why, comes Pete Best, the man who got kicked out of the Beatles. He's doing just fine. (As a subscriber to his website, I keep up on these things.) I read a little while ago that his band was on tour in Brazil, and recently I saw his handsome, healthy face in a CNN quiz. Married to the same woman for forty years. A sturdy lot, those Liverpudlians.

And now we're back at the beginning again, back to Raissa Shestatsky, the memory of whom, it would seem, began this slow swim back up the river. I did see her one more time. Well, not exactly *her*. I was walking toward the library at Victoria University in Toronto, where I'm teaching these days (a lucky break), when I saw a beautiful young girl sitting on a bench with a friend; dark coat, dark hair, dark eyes. It was a fall day, leaves on the ground, squirrels running here and there, and as I approached her, I felt almost embarrassed by her extraordinary beauty. I went up the stairs and through the glass doors into the library, and as a clutch of students pushed by me, I turned around for a last look. It was not a look of longing or desire or even curiosity, but something else; it felt as if I was on the verge of remembering something. But what was it? It was Raissa she reminded me of. Raissa, my long-lost beauty. Raissa, my love.

"What a privilege it is to be alive," I say to Nick. We are still in the park.

"What makes you say that?" he asks.

"More and more things these days."

It's time for us to get back to the hotel. We have a long day tomorrow, a live breakfast television show then lunch with someone and then some print media. I'm pooped. Besides which, tomorrow is my birthday; I want to be in good form. Nick wants to hang around in the lobby for a while, maybe have a drink in the bar. See what time the girl at the desk gets off work, who knows? I want my bed. At my age, beds have become something mostly for sleep. I say good night to him, good night to Sunset Strip, good night to the little park where I once suffered but to which I have now happily returned. Just thinking about all this, how long life is, how much happens, puts my head quickly on the pillow, and after only a few moments, the sound of a car horn, a voice in the hallway, I am asleep.